Dear Goswami,

A little inspiration for an inspired (and) person.

Have a great Christmas.

Your own, as ever,

Lucy

December, 2010

A RUNAWAY GOAT

Curing blindness in forgotten India

Lucy Mathen

Pause for Space Publications

Published by Pause for Space Publications, 2010

ISBN 0-9543662-7-1

For orders : please email:-

goat@Secondsight.org.uk

www.pauseforspacepublications.com

Introduction

Lucy Mathen is the most colossal pain in the arse. I speak with authority: I have known her since December 1974. It was the Christmas party for the Surrey Mirror in Redhill. I spotted a gorgeous girl, Asian of feature, drinking Pernod from a pint mug. Naturally, I made a pass at her. I claim to this day that a kiss was landed; she says that if so, she didn't notice. See what I mean?

We became friends instead. And I soon found she had a different idea of newspapers to every one else. She wanted to use journalism to benefit humankind. She wanted her writings to bring about justice and peace. As a result, she had a stand-up row with the editor, who binned a wholly legitimate piece about local coppers accused of beating up juvenile tearaways. The editor didn't want to upset the police; Lucy wanted to fight for the underdog. The editor thought Lucy was a pain in the arse.

Lucy then went into television journalism. She could have been a star. She had the looks, but she didn't have the temperament. She was too interested in justice and truth. She never wanted to sell herself, silly girl. It was always the bloody story, always truth and bloody justice.

Then she had a Damascene conversion and decided that journalism was False and Shallow, and that there were more direct ways of saving humankind. So she ditched her entire career and trained to be a doctor. Starting with A level Chemistry. Going through medical school with cocky sprogs fresh out of public school. Bearing her second child on the way.

I remember when she failed a rather important exam. I commiserated with her. "Good thing," she said. "I was starting to believe I was superwoman." So now she is humble as well. Sometimes, anyway.

So she became Dr Mathen, and specialised in ophthalmology, as she had always intended. And helped people and cured people and saved people's eyes and it was all very splendid. But Lucy being Lucy, it wasn't enough. And while looking after people's eyes was good, surely making the blind see was even better. Especially if they were the eyes of the underdog.

So she made yet another u-turn. She founded a charity, Second Sight, dedicated to making the blind see. Dedicated to getting skilled surgeons out to remote places in India where people walk blind because there are no clever hands out there to perform the humdrum miracle of the cataract operation.

She works from home, employs no people, takes not a cent in salary. Every penny raised, every pound, dollar, cent, paisa and rupee, goes straight to the task of making the blind see.

It's not the way most charities are run. It's not the way the big international charities dedicated to saving sight are run. Lucy has inevitably clashed with them. They think she is a pain in the arse. She doesn't care. She is out to help the underdog, to make blind people see in places where most people and most charities are reluctant or even afraid to travel.

She has had bruising encounters with bureaucrats and churchmen and politicos: Lucy, not being affected with the condition herself, can spot a phoney at 300 paces – and then makes her feelings about phoniness unambiguously clear. The people who find Lucy the biggest pain in the arse are all phonies.

When Lucy gets going, strong men duck, go pale, cross the M25. Lucy on a moral crusade is a fearsome sight. So perhaps I have drawn a picture of somebody who is self-righteous, strident, humourless and condemning. What a laugh.

Humour is the world's humanising trait. Without humour, we are lost. Without laughter, life is not worth living. And it is humour that saves Lucy from herself, as it saves us all. Lucy's capacity to relish the absurd, even or especially when it she is the butt of the joke, is essential for any one who spends a long time in India. I think the cow's urine story is my favourite.

Lucy's story is at bottom very simple. She wants to do good. And she finds the idea of compromising that simple notion impossible to contemplate. An approach to life that simply scares the crap out of some people, especially if they happen to be phonies.

But do you know something? She is not only fierce, she is actually right. Lucy is a tigress: but a tigress with all the best jokes.

November 2010

Simon Barnes

CONTENTS

NATARAJA

The Hindu God Nataraja stands with his right foot planted firmly on the dwarf demon Apasmara, the representation of sloth, ignorance and forgetfulness. His uplifted left leg is in graceful dance pose, foot neither flexed nor pointed, calf taut. He has four arms: the right back hand holds an hour-glass shaped drum, representing the rhythmic sound of the universe; the front right hand has the palm turned outward with fingers pointing upwards, a "fear not" gesture; the back left hand carries fire in a vessel, destructive energy; the front left arm is crossed over the body in elephant-trunk pose, pointing down to that all important dancing foot which can release a mature soul from bondage.

The goddess of the River Ganges nestles in his dreadlocks. It is said that the holy river originally flowed in heaven and when needed on earth, she hesitated because she realized that her fall from heaven would be too much for the earth to withstand. Nataraja agreed to break her fall by catching her in his tangled hair. The matted hair is also decorated with a crescent moon, the waxing and waning of the moon creating different seasons and rejuvenating life.

The all-devouring form looming over him is Mahakala "Great Time". The cobra around his waist is Kundalini Shakti, the cosmic power resident in each being.

The Lord Nataraja has a serene expression, yet he dances in a frenzy, continuously, within a circle of fire. He is dancing for the sheer joy of creation.

Nataraja's dance is not just symbolic. We would all do well to dance in that circle of fire. If we cannot muster sheer joy for what we do, we should at least be able to summon up some passion.

PART ONE

It all began in Rajasthan

Chapter One

Our magic for your magic

Rajasthan, July 2000

A rather battered white Maruti car pulled up in front of Jawai Bandh railway station. Its driver, a lean, bespectacled, grey-haired man dressed in white shirt and lungi, exited nimbly. He passed a group of shepherds with flame-red turbans and elaborate moustaches who touched their chests in respect, the station master in his smart black jacket and polished shoes who smiled in recognition; he gave a wide berth to the scores of families hustling their way onto the train, past porters with metal arm-bands around their red shirts and towers of luggage on their heads; with a small shake of his head he rejected a cup of water offered to him by a woman beside a huge earthenware container. He headed for the carriages at the far end of the train.

I recognized him immediately. A few months earlier in London I had sat through an excruciatingly embarrassing TV documentary made to raise money for a large international charity. It featured two British comedians who visited a remote eye hospital in Rajasthan. Dwelling on the physical discomforts of this comedic duo, the documentary-makers gave only a bit-part to the man who actually ran the hospital. Rajmal Jain had founded the Shree Bhairav Eye Hospital in his small ancestral village of Bisalpur. The hospital's achievements were spectacular. And within minutes of my meeting Rajmal it was clear to me that the producers had missed the best story by not making *him* the star of their documentary.

It was an auspicious meeting. Rajmal and I were in such good moods. I was happy because I had gone to sleep in the train with the dirt and grime of old Delhi rushing past the window, and had awoken to see the beautiful craggy hills of Rajasthan, a landscape with occasional splashes of spectacular colour and the glint of sunlight on the mirror-work patterned skirts of women carrying earthen pots on their heads. Rajmal was exceptionally happy because, after seven years of drought, the first monsoon rains had arrived and the wild peacocks were dancing in the hills behind his hospital.

When I stepped down onto the station platform I saw the people at closer quarters, noted the delicate embroidery on the dapper little white cotton waistcoats worn by the men and the small red stones set in gold petals that are the typical male earrings. I realised that what had looked like ivory bangles covering most of the arms of most of the women were in fact plastic bracelets. I saw Dick Whittington bundles slung from staffs and baby goats slung over shoulders. I met a fat businessman with a briefcase who touched Rajmal's feet in respect. And I saw, for the first time, those unmistakeable heavy black sunglasses worn with pride by every post-operative cataract patient in India.

Rajmal drove me to the eye hospital, hustling the many scooter-rickshaws and cycles to move out of his path on the very narrow tarmacked road. We passed a man on a camel.

"In London, you are having camels?" he asked.

"Only in zoos" I responded.

"Here it is Rajasthani transport" he laughed. And then, with great gusto added:

"But here is coming eye hospital transport."

And there it was, turning swiftly into the hospital grounds, hooting its arrival triumphantly, the big white bus that brought in the blind. It spewed out patients, and more patients, and patients' relatives. The vehicle held at least three times the amount of people that it was built for.

A skinny man with a mop of bright orange hennaed-hair jumped down from the driver's seat. He lit up a bidi. Hospital driver Champalal then gave me a succinct description of the hospital's modus operandi. It was like a poem.

"This day, two hundred kilometres.
Pick up patient. Thirty patient, thirty attendants.
Now, pre-operative check.
Tomorrow, surgery.
Next day, two hundred kilometres back. I am driving."

Inside the building Rajmal was already installed behind a desk in the huge, airy lobby and in deep conversation with a woman crouched at his feet. She was obviously worried about something. He took off his glasses and rubbed both his eyes, hard. Then he replaced the glasses. The woman looked reassured.

Rajmal explained to me that it was common for patients to worry that the plastic lens placed inside the eye during cataract surgery would fall out. Of course it is impossible. The IOL (intra-ocular lens) is deep inside the eye not on the surface.

"You are ophthalmologist, you know IOL cannot come out," he told me. "But I have been cataract patient. So I am showing in my way. Patient is now happy."

Fantastic. The late Sir Harold Ridley, the inventor of the intra-ocular lens, had to fight a prolonged battle with almost the entire medical establishment before they accepted that putting a plastic lens inside the eye was safe. He carried out his first IOL implantation in 1950 but in the United States the IOL was only approved as being "safe and effective" in 1981! How it would have warmed the cockles of his heart to see Rajmal's simple way of allaying the fears of illiterate villagers.

In the Shree Bhairav's modern operating theatre two surgeons had their heads bowed over the microscope eye-pieces. Gowned assistants concentrated on their movements and anticipated their need of particular instruments without the surgeons having to speak.

At first glance it could have been an eye theatre anywhere in the world. Then I saw the weather-beaten feet protruding from under the theatre drapes, one set of female ankles encircled with those ubiquitous heavy silver anklets. A third patient was being prepared for surgery by a scrub-nurse, her head still uncovered. An elaborate golden nose-ring gleamed under the lights. In a corner of the room, squatting patiently, was another woman with a patch over one eye, waiting for a paramedic to be freed up to take her back to the ward.

There was something very consoling about this juxtaposition of the latest in technology with ancient lifestyles; of Indian villagers receiving the same surgery to remove their cataracts as patients in Mumbai, London or New York; of microsurgery restoring sight to people who lived without running water or electricity and who preserved the connection with the earth and nature that is lost in India's cities.

One evening, a year later, when I had started sending volunteer eye surgeons to Bisalpur to work alongside their resident doctors, a group of magicians appeared at the guest-house. They were four bearded and moustachioed elderly men, with enormous hoop earrings dangling from long Buddha-like lobes; they wore orange shirts, orange turbans and white lungis. They came with their bag of tricks. Staff and visiting doctors crowded together in one room and we were treated to a show of "magic", a very amateur show of magic it has to be said, but fun anyway. We were told that they had come because one of them had had successful cataract surgery at the hospital. At the end of the show, this man turned to the doctors and said simply: "Our magic for your magic."

The Shree Bhairav is probably one of the most successful rural eye hospitals in India, although you are unlikely to have heard of it as Rajmal does not seek the limelight. It has received some international funding and the usual policy-directives from the funders. Yet is has remained quintessentially Rajasthani. Magic and microsurgery go hand in hand, there is a quiet courtesy towards patients, and Rajmal Jain and all who share his life even briefly can straddle the world of modern science and traditional beliefs with great enjoyment.

Looking back on all this with the hindsight of ten years involved in curing blindness in India, I fully appreciate how lucky we were that this was our starting point. And that I was lucky enough to meet Rajmal Jain so early on. I find it utterly baffling but it is a fact that there are people involved in the eradication of blindness who have no empathy for blind people and no passion for curing them. Recognizing and steering clear of these groups has been harder work than actually curing blind patients in the most neglected areas of India. Rajasthan and the Shree Bhairav Eye Hospital became my lode stone. I returned there whenever I felt pressured to run with the herd, whenever I found myself questioning dominant policies and opinions within the Charity World. I returned there to remind myself that humanitarian work is and should be straight-forward. If you want to restore sight to the blind, there really should be no excuses stopping you doing precisely that.

Chapter Two

Second only to God

It was 2am in a clammy mid-monsoon New Delhi. I wanted to arrive at my guest-house at a more reasonable hour so decided to hang around the airport for a while. I chose a grey plastic bucket-seat next to a middle-aged Indian man with an Indian Airlines identity card hanging around his neck.

"You are from?"
"England."
"Very good.Very good."
"Married?"
"Yes."
"Children?"
"Two. One girl, one boy."
"Very good."
"Profession?"
"Doctor."
"Accha" and a long sigh. " Madam Doctor. Doctor Madam. Very good."
He raised one hand and made a familiar Indian gesture, like twisting an enormous light bulb, once.
"Madam Doctor" he repeated. "Second only to God."

"Husband. Also doctor?"
"No. Computers."
A knowing head-wobble.
"Marriage made in heaven" he uttered wistfully and drifted off into smiling thoughts.

Now that's what I should have said to them during my medical school interview when they grilled me for 45minutes as to why, at the age of 36, as a successful TV reporter, I had decided to study Medicine. Your life is so glamorous, well-paid, interesting, the trio of besuited men across the desk had said, over and over again. So why do you want to give it up? Do you realise that doctors have amongst the highest rates of divorce and alcoholism? So had journalists, I replied.

Yes, but do you realise how mundane some of doctoring is, they persisted.

So can journalism be mundane and boring I riposted. Or worse I thought as I had a flashback to my days on a Breakfast Television station when I had to curtail an interview with Joshua Nkomo (an absolute scoop that the station should have been proud of) to make way for the Skateboarding Duck.

The medical interviewing team were being practically reverential in their assessment of journalism and almost scathing about their own profession. I am surprised I didn't blurt out: where have you guys been? Don't you know that journalists are said to be amongst the most detested of professionals and doctors the most respected? And here, twenty years later, was the proof. I was "second only to God."

I am joking of course. No doctor that I have ever met wants to be thought of in this way. It is far too scary. But in India, they deal in hyperbole. And everyone dreams of a son or daughter becoming a doctor. It is one of those running jokes on British TV comedy programmes like Goodness Gracious Me. And real life, too. Comedian Sanjeev Bhaskar tells of announcing to his parents that he wanted to be an "actor". In our family we pronounce that doctor said his father. Perhaps it's an apocryphal tale but very funny so worth repeating...although not to my airport companion who would not have seen any humour in it at all. He would have preferred the true tale that I told the interviewing panel.

The year before I entered medical school I was in Kabul. It was the year 1988, and the Russians were pulling out of Afghanistan. It was a time when so many bombs were dropping on the capital city that the British Foreign Office had warned us not to go. The roads out of town were full of speeding Soviet tanks manned by tense soldiers. I went with an all-female film crew. We were fed up with reports from male reporters dressed in Afghan clothes, ducking bullets as they roamed around with various armed groups. We wanted to know what the women and children were doing.

It was absolutely fantastic. We found, as expected, women doing just about everything and expressing just about every point of view. The true containment of free speech and freedom to simply live we found later when we spent a week in the dreadful Afghan refugee camps in the Pakistani town of Peshawar.

On our last day in Kabul we were taken by our Afghan government 'minders' to a clinic outside the city. The male doctor did not look a happy man and slunk away as if he being part of the filming was the last thing on his mind. Later he attached himself to me and whispered that he would tell me the "true story." It was easy to distract our minders so that the camera operator and I could interview the doctor in a back room.

His story was not world-shattering: only one of out-of-date drugs and a chaotic health-care system. He was telling us these facts in the belief that disclosure might result in action to change things. He was pale, gaunt, and full of pent-up anger and frustration. Fleetingly, I recalled a very different man: dark, muscle-bound, clenching and unclenching his fists as they lay on the table between us. He was shaking with nerves, sweat on the brow, while I laughed in disbelief and asked him why he was so frightened of me. He was a leading Sri Lankan Tamil Tiger commando and I was interviewing him at a secret location in south India. He had killed many people. But with my radio microphone pointed at him he crumpled into a nervous wreck and stammered his way through the interview. He admitted to being terrified because he said "your weapon is more powerful than mine."

At that time, I believed him. I thought the world could be changed through journalism. But ten years later, interviewing the Afghan doctor, I felt a fraud. Our camera team would be out of Kabul in 24hours, we would include his interview in a Channel 4 documentary shown to a small audience, and then what?

I decided that if I were ever in a war zone again, I would be a medic not a journalist. There is a high chance that the Afghan doctor responsible for this epiphany is no longer alive.

Chapter Three

Cadavers and career paths

St.George's Hospital Medical School, London

It was time to take the sheets off.

Each table had six medical students around it and, as if the whole event had been perfectly choreographed, when the Anatomy Demonstrator said the word, one person from each team lifted the edge of the sheet and peeled it back from the body.

A young girl let out a yelp. And dashed out of the room.

The rest of the 149 of us peered down with interest at our cadavers.

On our table, Matt, a doctor's son, the sheet-remover, said:

"What shall we call him then?"

Everyone laughed. A few remarks were exchanged about the body: looks as if he's smiling doesn't he, quite fit for a 75year-old, large head.

"Let's call him Fred."

This came from Sheena, a lass from the Shires with clipped tones and a dreamy manner.

The table approved of Sheena's choice of name. So Fred it was.

The young woman who had exited earlier in a state of shock now re-entered the room and approached the Head of Anatomy. He was a debonair man whose dazzling white shirt cuffs and gold cufflinks highlighted the drabness of his outer garment, the ubiquitous white coat. He bent his dark head towards her and listened. They came to an agreement. She joined our table. She didn't seem to have a problem with Fred.

"Ok?" asked cheery Matt.

"Yes thanks. It was just that...the other one looked like my Granny."

Ah, we murmured sympathetically. Matt chuckled.

I came to learn that every time Matt chuckled it was because he could see the makings of a story: he was the editor of the student rag and, like all good journalists, saw Copy everywhere. Sharing dissection classes with Matt was like being at the editorial meetings of a tabloid newspaper. As we took it in turns to wield the scalpel and peel back skin, muscle, connective tissue and fat, as we marvelled at the delicate nerves that once innervated Fred's powerful body, we also gossiped and got to know each other. Matt sniffed out stories like a good newshound.

Before the summer Ball, Matt asked Sheena to write a column about where to buy the best ball gowns and I was amazed at the sartorial and retail knowledge that Sheena displayed.

It was also over Fred's dead body that I learned from Sheena of the tensions between her and her best friend Roz. The two lived in a kind of symbiotic existence, roaming the Med School with linked arms, sitting next to each other at every lecture, and living in adjacent rooms in the halls of residence. Sheena was the posher, the more sophisticated, the cleverer. Medicine was simply what clever girls at her school chose to study. Roz was a no-nonsense Brummie from a state school who desperately wanted to be a doctor.

Roz was gone by the end of the first year, furious with herself for failing the exams and refusing to re-sit. The saddest thing for me, as a mature student at medical school, was seeing the young men and women who probably would have made the best doctors fall at the first hurdles…those wretched exams that most of us passed by regurgitating information that we forgot the moment we exited the examination room.

"What do you think about having a column for the Matures" asked Matt one day as we stripped Fred's right leg down to the bone. "We could call it …Wrinklies at St.George's Hospital Medical School…something like that."

"Not enough of us" I retorted, showing admirable restraint at not objecting to being referred to as a wrinkly.

The 'matures' made up only about ten percent of the students each year. We ranged in age from early 20s (those coming straight from another degree or who had flunked their A levels first time), to late 20s (an osteopath, a dentist, a teacher) and, traditionally, one complete eccentric in their 30s. Like me. The previous year it had been my friend Julie, a trade unionist who also shared with me a history of attending evening classes at London's Hackney College. A Grade B in A level Chemistry was a pre-requisite for entry to St.George's if your first degree was in an Arts subject.

Historically, dissection at St.George's began with the Upper Limb and then progressed down to the foot, with a quick detour to cover the Head and Neck at about Xmas time in the first term. For most of the time we kept Fred's face covered. It seemed appropriate. Each week his body looked more and more ravished by our archaeological digs.

At the end of the year, like all the cadavers, Fred had a proper burial and we were encouraged to attend. I suggested to Matt that he should write Fred's obituary. He liked the idea. I could call it "Over His Dead Body", he said.

That boy was made for the tabloids.

Those first two pre-clinical years at St.George's were a kind of limbo. Relentlessly punctuated by exams, we put our heads down, learned numerous mnemonics to aid our recall of a ludicrous number of facts, and whooped with joy each time we managed to scrape through to the next round.

All that changed dramatically in the third year when we were thrown onto the wards and the reality of being a real doctor became a closer goal. Many students also realised how their aspirations had changed. A show of hands during a first year lecture showed that becoming a general practitioner was low on anyone's priority; yet most people were happy to become GPs by the end. Choosing a hospital specialty was not often dictated by the difficulty or ease with which one could get into the department; we were most influenced by the way that the qualified doctors behaved towards us and how happy they appeared to be. So while orthopaedics was a truly fun specialty, the orthopods, with a few exceptions, were such bullies, such mysogonistic arrogant men (then exclusively men at St.George's) that we revolted at the thought of joining them, no matter how much we enjoyed screwing in nails to prostheses and getting pleasure from the sheer 'fixing' that orthopaedics offers.

Where was I heading? Rapidly eliminating most fields, sadly, the more frustrated and unhappy doctors that I met. I had, after all, had a mostly pleasurable first career as a journalist. I did not associate work with being miserable.

And then we had a two week attachment to the Ophthalmology Department. Call me a simpleton but, a group of happy doctors and my first sight of the optic disc viewed in full magnified splendour through an ophthalmoscope was enough to make me want to deal with eyes for the rest of my medical career. What I did not anticipate was that Ophthalmology would come to dominate my life.

Chapter Four

Turning away the blind

Tamil Nadu, India

There were long lines of them, each person with one hand placed on the shoulder of the man or woman in front, picking their way cautiously through the car-park. Most had bare feet and the faded saris and dhotis of poor people who wash the same set of clothes over and over again because that's all they have. Hospital staff ushered them up the ramp and into the building. They disappeared from our sight.

We took the stairs to the second floor and headed for the small room in which we had spent every morning for the last five days crouched over microscopes. We took our usual places and began. On small pieces of foam we practised our suturing. We sewed with special concentration this morning because it was the last opportunity we had before we would be using the same technique on human eyes. That earlier sighting of the patients coming in for surgery helped to concentrate our minds.

A fellow ophthalmologist from Britain and I were taking part in a surgical course at a famous Eye Institute in south India. It is now the largest and most productive eye hospital in the world, in terms of surgical numbers and patients treated. We were kind of gate-crashers: the hospital ran a Microsurgery Course for Indian doctors and we had managed to get onto it, I think, simply because we were the first foreign doctors to ask. We were also paying $20 a day to stay in the foreign guest-house.

We were both in our first ophthalmic jobs and desperate for some hands-on surgical experience. At the hospital where we worked in England, the senior doctors were themselves swapping over to a new method of cataract surgery. Consultants were using operating theatre time to learn themselves. They were, somewhat understandably, loathe to use this time to teach absolute beginners. Geeta Menon, an Indian colleague at our hospital told us about the south Indian training course.

When we arrived to start this course, the extent of our surgical experience was "watering the cornea" which meant squirting saline solution from a syringe over the eye to keep it moist while the surgeon was doing the clever stuff. On the 8-week surgical course, we were given an individual tutor, and taken through the steps of cataract surgery at our own pace until we were safe to operate independently. Then, being the busiest eye unit in the world, there were plenty of patients for everybody. As trainees and experienced surgeons worked side by side in large operating theatres, you could always call for help if an operation proved difficult and a more experienced surgeon would be at your side in seconds. It was a good system.

It did feel, however, more like an efficient factory than a hospital. The bosses (a family of south Indian ophthalmologists) were uncompromising, dictatorial and not always consistent. In lectures they preached the doctrine of respecting each poor patient as much as a wealthy patient, but, I for one, rarely saw them show much kindness to either patients or trainees. The bulk of the hard work and all our surgical training was carried out by other doctors: amazingly skilled and dedicated surgeons, mostly poorly-paid Fellows. My own personal tutor was a lovely man called Dr.Mohan who celebrated my achievements with laughter and smiles and once cried with me (literally) when I made the same surgical mistake in two concurrent operations. The doctor in charge of the entire course, Arup Chakrabarti, was a thoroughly fair, even-tempered man with a quiet sense of irony. Chatting about the world as we scrubbed before operating sessions laid the foundations of a relationship that I was to pick up on years later.

Each operating day, we were given torches and told to walk the corridors. There, squatting quietly, backs up against the walls, were hundreds of pre-operative patients, most of them completely blind. Our task was to find the few amongst them who were *not* blind. Operating on early (immature) cataracts is easier than operating on hyper-mature cataracts. We were beginners so had to choose our patients carefully both for our sakes and theirs.

One day fellow trainee Dr.Avinesh and I walked down the line, shining our torches into eyes now widely dilated by pre-operative drops. All we saw were the milky-white or dark brown pupils characteristic of very advanced cataracts. But the patients were so hopeful; they were calling out in the local language and reaching out to touch us.

I crouched in front of a tiny woman with grey hair. I was hoping that her cataract would be of the right kind and that I would be able to pin a small label with my name on it onto her tattered sari.

Further up the line, another surgical trainee called to us that there were a few "good cases" at his end and that we should come.

I switched the torch off and began to get up from my squat. I found the index finger of my left hand gripped with the strength of a newborn baby's involuntary grasp reflex. The little woman muttered earnestly to me, refusing to let go. It was impossible to pry her fingers off mine.

"What is she saying?" I asked Avinesh.

"She is asking you to choose her" he said. "But Dr.Lucy you must not. We have to have easy cases. Don't worry they all get done by someone. Come, we must go. We are supposed to be in theatre by now."

Of course he was right. I would probably have messed up her operation if I had taken it on because I was not experienced enough. And she would have her sight restored that day anyway, like everyone else. But in that moment when we were linked in that vice-like grip, all she was aware of was that she was blind and that I was rejecting her. It was a horrid moment.

After four weeks in south India I had become almost blasé about seeing hundreds of blind people coming to the hospital each day. That one personal encounter, however, unsettled me. I would never be able to forget the urgency transmitted in her grasp and how it conveyed to me the cocktail of hope, panic and fear that a blind patient must feel when examined by an eye surgeon.

Chapter Five

Worm's eye view

"When you can hold the world in your palm and can see it from a bird's eye view, you tend to become arrogant – you do not realise that when looking from such a great distance, everything becomes blurred, and that you end up imagining rather than really seeing things."

Muhammad Yunus

When economist Muhammad Yunus realised that the economic theories he had been teaching his students in Bangladesh had not prevented thousands from starving to death, he decided he would "become a student all over again", leave the ivory tower of Chittagong University and get into the villages.

He acknowledged (and then proved with the spectacular track record of his micro-credit Grameen Banks) what all those working in the humanitarian field should admit: that you have to look at things at close range in order to see them sharply. If you really want to help people a worm's eye view of their predicament is far superior to that of the soaring bird. Even if, at first, you deliver small scale help, at least it is real help rather than theory. Small when effective is indeed beautiful. And small successes replicated can achieve great aims. Aim to cure blindness one eye at a time in just one place and you may well eliminate unnecessary blindness from the entire world. The worm's eye view does not mean you cannot still see the sky and reach for the stars.

Sometime in the year 1999, I was deeply immersed in my own ophthalmic training, struggling with the remorseless process of working long hours whilst at the same time studying for interminable (and expensive) specialist examinations, all supposedly leading to that Holy Grail of a Consultant's post in the National Health Service. In other words the average doctor's lot.

Then one Saturday morning I read an editorial in the British Journal of Ophthalmology about the Initiative Vision 2020 A Right to Sight, launched by the World Health Organisation and the International Agency for the Prevention of Blindness. The editorial was a clarion call to all ophthalmologists to get involved in this admirable cause: to eliminate reversible blindness by the year 2020.

With the cynicism born of 15 years as a journalist during which I had covered many a launching of a humanitarian initiative that had withered on the vine, I muttered. Just watch them all, I told friends, they will sit around holding conferences and discussing strategies and the blind will remain blind. And what about you, asked a few. Seem to remember that you came back from that trip to India vowing to do something about cataract blindness. If you think you could do better, do it.

This was all true. But could I do better? Could I really do anything? India was a good place to start. It was the country of my birth. Also the country with the worst blindness problem. And I knew India pretty well, knowledge gained from quite different observational posts. When he was alive, I frequently visited my father in Mumbai. He was from the generation that had lived under the British Raj and had then experienced the exhilaration and surge of enthusiasm that came with building a newly liberated nation. He was India's second most senior commercial pilot, the first being his friend the legendary JRD Tata who founded the national airline Air India. My Dad rose to the ranks of senior management at Air India but, unusual for a manager, continued to fly his beloved jumbo jets until the day he retired. His circle of friends were highly educated, well-off and well-travelled. But like so many of that first generation of free Indians he felt a little guilty about the sorry predicament of most of his fellow Indians. Perhaps that was why he took such keen interest in my journalistic exploits whenever I visited. I would combine my trips with assignments: covering a strike by 250,000 factory workers in Maharashtra or recording the lives of bonded labourers at brick kilns in Haryana. Using my Dad's flat in Mumbai as my base, I travelled extensively within India's borders and with a journalist's privileged access to both the wealthy and the dirt-poor I began to get a feel of the complexity of the country of my birth.

Later, as a doctor and an ophthalmologist, I was once again put in a privileged position. During the south Indian surgical training course I saw the horrific scale of India's cataract blindness problem but also a system for coping with it: hospitals providing high-volume, low-cost, good quality cataract surgery. I had experienced the direct doctor-patient relationship but far removed from my own British working environment. I had trained alongside Indian doctors and experienced the rigid hierarchy of Indian medical training. But as a foreign trainee, I had also witnessed the very different relationship between the powerful family who ran the hospital and visiting 'partners' either international funders or volunteers. And of course, each time I recalled that course, there was a sharp visual memory of the small blind woman who had begged me to operate on her.

In the end, however, what spurred me into action was neither the pull of emotion nor a rigorous analysis of what I had to offer, but a strong hunch.

When questioned about why India had accumulated such a huge backlog of people needlessly blind from cataract, the reasons given by national bodies and international charities were: the lack of infrastructure in rural areas, the lack of training, the lack of equipment and the ignorance of uneducated people. Meanwhile another, to my mind, supremely important factor was being glossed over: eighty per cent of India's ophthalmologists were working in urban areas and in private practice; the vast majority of India's blind people lived in the villages with no access to eye surgeons.

Could it be that, at the start of the 21st.century, the main reason why India's blind were staying blind was simply because eye surgeons were unwilling to work in the impoverished and forgotten areas? Was this why India, in spite of having enough eye surgeons even for its huge population, in spite of manufacturing at low cost, all the equipment necessary for cataract surgery, still had more people unnecessarily blind from cataract than any other nation?

If this were true, then I could really do something about it. In Britain there were numerous ophthalmologists who, like me, were of Indian origin. Surely this Diaspora of doctors could provide a source of experienced eye surgeons willing to work for short periods at rural hospitals lacking surgeons? Then, leading by example, we could try and persuade Indian surgeons to give up their time to do the same. If the eye surgeon was the missing link in the chain between the blind patient and sight-restoring cataract surgery then the problem was not without a solution. Could it really be that simple? If it was, then I might just be the person to launch such a project. I was good at persuading. Persuading my colleagues to cure the blind would, surely, be a doddle. But was I right that the lack of eye surgeons was the biggest reason for the blind remaining blind?

There was only one full-proof way to confirm that my hunch was correct. I took time out from Ophthalmology in London, flew to Delhi and hit the road. It was time to get that worm's eye view.

Chapter Six

Moving mountains

My first contacts in India were two large charitable hospitals based in Delhi but with programmes to tackle blindness in the rural areas of Haryana and Rajasthan states. They kindly took me to most of their satellite eye units and were open to the idea of accommodating visiting volunteer eye surgeons, especially those of Indian origin. This reverse brain drain appealed to them as they had a huge problem in persuading Indian doctors to leave the capital city. However, I was surprised by the lack of patients at these units. An estimated ten million blind people in India and hospitals run by well-known eye institutes short of patients? It didn't make sense.

I needed to go into the heart of the Indian countryside. I needed to find the blind. I knew the location of at least one eye hospital teeming with patients. The hospital featured in the TV documentary. I caught the overnight train from Old Delhi station and headed deep into Rajasthan.

Rajmal Jain sat in his favourite place at the Shree Bhairav Eye Hospital: behind a desk which was strategically placed in the corner of the vast hospital lobby so that he could see everyone who entered and, more importantly, so that he was visible and accessible to all. I think he also enjoyed the sight of the gleaming stone floor which was cleaned a dozen times a day by a tall elegant woman called Tara, who moved along its expanse in an easy squat, making extensive sweeps of her wet cloth and, from time to time, rearranging her diaphanous head-scarf. Gnarled feet with heavy silver anklets, dusty curly-toed Rajasthani slippers, an occasional wheelchair and the even less frequent polished shoes of a private patient, all these left their temporary marks. But somehow Tara kept the floor shining and pristine.

While Rajmal's view from behind his desk was wide-angle, my view, sitting with my back to the lobby, was zoomed in. It was impossible, when sitting in front of that desk, to prevent your eyes being drawn to a sign above Rajmal's head. It says:

"A patient is the most important visitor than any other on our premises. He is not dependent on us. We are dependent on him. He is not an interruption on our work. He is the purpose of it. We are not doing him a favour by serving him. He is doing us a favour by giving us an opportunity to do so."

Underneath is written

"Rajmal S Jain

Chairman, Shree Bhairav Eye Hospital"

The quote is actually a bowdlerized version of a famous quote by Mahatma Gandhi. But heh, great minds think alike. And Rajmal really has a great mind, a big heart and a free spirit.

"I am simple man" he likes to tell strangers, meaning uneducated because his schooling was incomplete. He was the eldest of ten children and with that role went a responsibility to help his parents with generating income for the entire family. He joined his father in Mumbai at the age of 10 but left school early to help with the family businesses in Textiles and Transport. His humanitarian leanings were evident early on and rapidly coloured his whole approach to life. During the 1950s there was a terrible flu epidemic in Bombay and thousands of slum-dwellers were dying. Rajmal discovered that while the medicine (penicillin) cost a few annas (a fraction of a rupee), doctors were charging four rupees to give the injections.

"I am learning then that in India, medicines are cheap but doctors expensive."

Rajmal bought a stash of penicillin, set up a stall in the slums and convinced a medical student to give the injections. Hundreds survived as a result. That was his first humanitarian project.

Back in his home-state of Rajasthan, cataract blindness was rampant. In almost every village there was a familiar sight: a small child holding one end of a pole and a blind person the other. Children were chosen to be the guides for blind adults who had no hope of ever being cured. Worse still, quacks professing that they could cure cataract blindness were operating all over remote areas, setting up unofficial eye 'camps' and carrying out botched surgery.

In 1968, a friend in Bombay, a witness to Rajmal's superb organisational ability, suggested that he should get involved in the much-needed area of eye-care for the poor. He agreed. He persuaded ophthalmologists from the big city to give their time free of charge. And he took care of the rest.

Not long after this a young British traveller was hiking around rural Rajasthan and was attracted by a group of stunningly colourful tents in the desert. He thought it was a circus. He wandered down and was greeted by the young Rajmal, overseeing hundreds of blind patients, attendants, paramedical staff and doctors. Rajmal showed him the Operation Theatre tent and the tents housing and feeding the patients. He invited the young traveller to help with distributing food to the patients.

A local army Brigadier Hare Singh watched from the sidelines. He was much impressed. Even in the army he had never seen such precision-planning. Nothing had been overlooked.

At that time, cataract surgery in India was a much more basic operation than it is now. The eye's lens, made cloudy or opaque by cataract, was removed wholesale without replacing it with a clear plastic intraocular lens. The patient was then given thick "cataract glasses" that enabled them to see, albeit with a magnification of one third. The operation was done without a microscope. And by the light of a powerful torch! In spite of this, hundreds of lives were transformed.

At the sixth camp organised by Rajmal a six year-old girl called Salu had successful cataract surgery. Salu lived till her mid-forties, using her good vision to live a full life, working, marrying and having children. Her picture remains over the gates of the Bhairav Eye Hospital, a constant reminder of the huge impact cataract surgery can make, even when it is done under a tent in the middle of the desert, as long as the eye surgeon and assistants follow a meticulous surgical protocol.

Rajmal was not, however, a man to remain behind the times. He realised that it was not the best solution to have temporary diagnostic and surgical camps in the desert.(The term eye camp, however, continues to be used to this day to describe the process of collecting patients from outlying areas and bringing them back to hospital for surgery).

More modern equipment was also needed. With intra-ocular cataract surgery and the insertion of a plastic lens into the eye now becoming the norm, microscopes, proper hospital buildings and properly trained permanent staff were necessary.

So Rajmal built a small 30bedded eye hospital in his ancestral village of Bisalpur. It was both an aesthetically-pleasing and practical one-storey building on the side of a road. But within a year he realised that it was too small if it was going to be the base for a huge programme to cure the blind in the entire area.

"Opposite hospital was mountain" he said showing me a black and white photograph of the area.

"We removed mountain. New hospital was built on site."

By the year 2000, when I first visited, the Shree Bhairav was housed in beautiful purpose-built premises, designed by Rajmal, with soothing blue window shutters, high ceilings and cool stone floors. It had good ophthalmic equipment and patient transportation vehicles, some of it still provided by an international charity.

But Rajmal knew that the hospital's ability to continue to cure the blind was precarious. It was still very difficult to recruit and retain good eye surgeons. The pull from the lucrative world of private medicine in the urban areas could be felt even in remote Rajasthan.

In the month of July 2000, six months after I had registered Second Sight as a UK charity, I made a formal offer to Rajmal to supply a rota of experienced volunteer eye surgeons for his hospital. His reply was unequivocal.

"For 20 years people are coming offering money, offering equipment. You are first person offering eye surgeons. We all need surgeons."

Hallelujah! I was on the right path. Following that hunch had been worth it.

Chapter Seven

Dire straits

I returned to London after that first fact-finding trip having travelled hundreds of miles across north India mostly by train, bus and occasionally bullock-cart. In the year 2000 there was not the plethora of small domestic airlines connecting up the country. Apart from the Shree Bhairav, I had visited over a dozen rural eye hospitals. I had found thousands of pounds worth of expensive ophthalmic equipment gathering cobwebs because they were no eye surgeons to operate. So I was eager to present my solution to this problem to the main organisation that had provided much of this equipment, a large British-based charity.

I met the then India Programme Officer. I explained that I had just returned from visiting hospitals that had been generously provided with expensive equipment by their organisation but which had no eye surgeons. These hospitals had asked us to provide visiting ophthalmologists to cure the cataract blind. We were happy to do so.

"Well, we can't stop you working in this way," he said. "And of course you don't need our support. But we can't give our approval."

Why ever not? I asked.

"We don't approve of expatriot doctors going to India and doing what the Indians should be doing," he replied.

"Not even when most of these surgeons are actually of Indian origin and initially trained in India?"

"Still expats."

"But these hospitals cannot get doctors from within the country. Doctors in India choose to work in private practise in the cities. What can you do about that?"

"That's actually not our brief," he replied. "It is the responsibility of the Indian hospitals to get surgeons."

"Okay, so let me get this straight," I said. "There is expensive equipment supplied by you sitting there unused, there are blind patients galore in those areas but no Indian doctors. You would prefer the equipment to be wasted, the blind to stay blind, rather than us sending experienced volunteer surgeons from Britain?"

There was a pause.

"If only it were that simple, Lucy" he smiled wearily.

I recalled my surgical training course in south India. I remembered the tiny south Indian woman with the iron grip, the patient who had held onto me when she thought she was being rejected for surgery. Ten million people blind from cataract in India and we were arguing about the *best* way to solve the problem! Surely we should be pulling out all stops?

I decided to telephone Rajmal Jain for a boost of confidence. Did he still want me to send surgeons?

"Yes,yes" he announced with certainty. "After Diwali we will have many patients."

Diwali was only a few months away.

In the corner of my bedroom where I had installed my 'office', I sieved through the mountains of letters that I had written to the richest British Asians (as listed by The Times) asking for financial support for Second Sight. All were rejections. At that stage we did not need a great deal of money: just enough to pay the travel expenses of the volunteer surgeons. The hospital would provide simple food and accommodation.

I re-read some of my letters. I would not have changed the wording on any of them but something was missing. As I sat there pondering this my 8year-old son Calum came into the room to say goodnight.

"Cal, you know how I explained that there are people in India who are blind and an operation can cure them?"

He nodded.

"Well I need a design, a logo. So when people see it they get that message. What would you draw?"

"I would draw one eye open and one eye shut" he replied.

"Brilliant. Can you do that for me?"

"I can do it on Paintbox" he said and climbed onto my lap to get at the computer.

After a few consultations about colouring, he had a lovely logo design.

"The only thing is...they have to be Indian eyes" I said.

With hardly a micro-pause he replied

"Then put the red dot on the forehead".

And within seconds it was there, a red bindi in the middle of two eyes. All that was left then was to add the Second Sight lettering on either side. At which stage, it really was time for bed.

I sent off another round of letters for funds, this time with Calum's eye-catching logo. A rush of replies did not result. And I dropped into despondency once again. One evening we found ourselves watching the Parkinson show on TV. Michael Parkinson was interviewing guitarist Mark Knopfler, one of my musical heroes. His band Dire Straits were having their first huge hits in the 1970s when I was playing in a small amateur pub band in south London and we occasionally fantasised about becoming as famous as them.

It was a relaxed interview and Mark Knopfler appeared very unaffected for a rock star of such longevity. The next day I mentioned this to a neighbour, also a musician, and he said: get Knopfler to do a charity gig for you.

So I called Mark Knopfler's PA Robyn Becker. Don't ask me how I got her number. Just remember that I was once a journalist. From her slightly harassed tone it sounded as if I had caught her at a particularly bad time. But I spoke from the heart and for not too long and something must have hit a spot because Robyn said:

"Lucy, if you can fax me an A4 sheet with the details, I'll put it under Mark's nose this afternoon. This sounds like a great charity."

A few days passed. Robyn rang. Just how much money did I need to get the show on the road? she asked. If I had £5000 in the bank I would send the first surgeon to Rajasthan I replied.

Another day went by. I was playing squash when my mobile phone rang. It was Robyn saying that they had discussed a charity gig and had decided that it was not possible at such short notice. I slumped down in the corner of the squash court, bitterly disappointed. Then Robyn told me that Mark Knopfler had decided to donate the £5,000 to get the charity off the ground. The money would be in the bank the next day. So get those surgeons out there, Lucy, she said.

"Oh, and Mark LOVED your son's logo".

Rock n' Roll!

Next, I rang the only person I was absolutely convinced should be the first Second Sight surgeon. He was a Consultant in Nottinghamshire but we had worked together at a London hospital and I had liked him enormously. Srinivasan Subramaniam was also of Indian origin, and had done his basic medical training and some ophthalmology in India before moving to Britain.

Without the slightest hesitation 'Mani' told me:

"Lucy, I have taken two weeks holiday over Christmas. But I can use it to go to Rajasthan for Second Sight. My family won't mind. My wife has been pushing me to do something like this for years."

So on December 25, 2000, Mani was in the operating theatre of the Shree Bhairav Eye Hospital and became the first Second Sight surgeon to carry out cataract surgery that restored sight to a blind Indian patient. Better still, he did something that none of the resident surgeons was at that time able to do. He carried out laser treatment on a 12year-old child called Hemaran. The boy had had surgery for congenital cataract that gave him sight for the first time. He had then developed a common complication with paediatric cases that can cause blindness once again. It requires simple laser treatment. The laser machine had been donated to the hospital but none of the local doctors had been trained to use it. By the time Mani had departed, successful laser treatment had guaranteed Hemaran's good sight, and the resident doctors had been trained to deal with similar cases.

Back in the year 2000, the hospital had no email. So Rajmal rang up to report on the great success of Mani's trip and to wish me Happy Xmas.

"What is you *next* programme for India?" he asked, making our small start sound like a huge enterprise already and causing a few butterflies to flutter. But that was Rajmal all over. And with him behind me there was no turning back.

Chapter Eight

Same same

By the end of our first year of existence, Second Sight's volunteer surgeons were working alongside the doctors of the Shree Bhairav Eye Hospital throughout the busy winter months. The resident ophthalmologists were Dr.Kaushlenra Kumar and Dr.Gulam Ali, both young men who had told me, when I first visited, that they did not intend to remain out in the sticks for more than a year or two. Like most of India's ophthalmologists, they were eager to get into the city and start their private practices. They were intrigued by the fact that doctors would come all the way from Britain, in their spare time and for no money, to help them cure the blind. Although they themselves were curing the blind on a daily basis, they did not seem to pat themselves on the back for this (in our eyes) extraordinarily important work in the land with the worst blindness problem!

They did enjoy, however, the constant exchange of clinical knowledge that went on when the visiting surgeons were there. The remote hospital had overnight become a more stimulating working environment.

Other hospitals in Rajasthan approached Rajmal asking if they could have visiting eye surgeons, too. But Rajmal had high standards and was not prepared to commit himself to recommending them as Second Sight partners.

"Not all same same like Bhairav Eye Hospital," he said.

But he offered to take me to them, every single one of them. The tour would take "three days only"…if we drove through the first night. We were to leave immediately. And Rajmal's Number 2 brother Kesari, who was visiting from Mumbai, would accompany us.

"Kesari is suffering diabetes" said Rajmal. "Also heart only fifteen per cent working."

So with driver Abaysingh at the wheel, Kesari with his dodgy heart and all of us having gone without supper, we sped into the night. Kesari and Rajmal chatted non-stop in Hindi and I wallowed in the beauty of the Rajasthani landscape lit up by a half-moon and coruscating stars. Occasionally Rajmal would remember to be a tour guide.

"Backside of mountain is tribal area" he said.

"Tribal families very poor."

Kesari added a comment in Hindi.

"Yes, yes" said Rajmal. "Kesari is saying tell Lucy tribal families are having love-marriage, not arranged marriage. Girl boy choosing."

And do the tribals come for surgery at the Shree Bhairav Hospital? I asked.

"Yes, yes. Now they are coming. Before there was no road. Then I am making road for them. Coming back we can see."

We stopped for food at a road-side restaurant and ate daal and roti. Eating the meal took only a few minutes but Rajmal and Kesari quizzed the cook for much longer beforehand about what kind of lentils he used and how he was going to cook them. I was beginning to think they were being pernickety old men when I remembered that they were Jains and that the daal must have no onions or garlic in it.

During the next leg of the journey the craggy hills interspersed with fields began to be replaced by sandier land. Wild deer turned their heads and pricked up their ears at the sound of our car. I dozed fitfully, awaking each time my lolling head hit the window, and each time I heard Rajmal and Kesari nattering away happily. Obviously the brothers had a lot of news to catch up on.

Just as the moon was losing its glow and a rosy flush announced dawn, the sand dunes began, getting steeper and steeper. We stopped to climb one. And I took a lovely picture of Rajmal, out of breath but smiling, with the sun making a brilliant cross behind him. That was the high spot of the trip. After that it got depressing.

At the first hospital we visited, we found good buildings, good equipment and a big white bus donated by international funders. We also found grubby premises, low staff morale and an over excited trustee who only wanted to take pictures. There was an ophthalmologist, an ex-Government doctor, who was trying his best. Sadly, he had so little surgical training that he was unable to do much cataract surgery. Looking on the bright side, I took his details and thought that perhaps we could send a Second Sight surgeon to train him.

At the second hospital, based in a large town, the operating theatre was being painted and the out-patients department was closed. The trustees we met told us that they had employed two ophthalmologists, a husband and wife team, who were due to join the hospital "within days." One of the trustees showed me the thick, detailed report that they had sent to their international funders and which had resulted in their ongoing funding for building work. Rajmal expressed doubt as to whether the ophthalmic couple would actually materialise.

The third hospital was in a perfect setting, small villages for miles around as far as the eye could see. The buildings were spacious, the equipment great, there was ample staff accommodation and even a primary school and small-scale shopping mall on the land! The person in charge was a Jain businesswoman who wore trousers and had closely cropped hair.

"Looking like man" commented Rajmal, but not in a derogatory tone.

She had spent years in Canada and seemed to be motivated to help the area in Rajasthan in which she had been born. She had put some of her own money into the enterprise. However, when left with me to see patients (the very few who had been brought in that day) the resident ophthalmologist blurted out that he hated the place, was terrified because he had no clinical back-up and that when he took his concerns to "ma'am" she had been most unhelpful. I promised that, as long as they could bring in lots of blind patients, I would send an experienced surgeon to work with him. Then he would not feel so clinically isolated and more work would be achieved. No, he said, dramatically, he had handed in his notice just that morning.

Best to leave this one out of the Second Sight equation, I decided.

At the fourth hospital, the situation looked encouraging. The building resembled the Shree Bhairav Hospital (Rajmal had actually designed it), there were a sufficient number of paramedics and even a recently-joined full-time ophthalmologist, a friendly Sikh from the Punjab.

There was also his mother. She was delighted to meet a doctor from London she said. Then altering her expression to that of a spoilt child she wailed:

"What is my son doing in this backward place?"

It was a bit rich this, addressing the question to me. I had just made my usual motivational speech to her son: about Second Sight surgeons discovering how exciting ophthalmology was in India's rural areas; about the many Indian ophthalmologists I had met who complained that in the cities they spent most of their time dealing with hypochondriacal patients with watery eyes. I did not dwell on the fact that they were also raking in the money.

Mummyji pouted at me and continued:

"You are an ophthalmologist. Tell him that he is wasting his talent. He could be in Delhi or Mumbai or...?"

Don't even go there, lady.

"What are you thinking?" asked Rajmal as I scowled in the back seat of the car as we drove off.

"Mummy's boy" I retorted.

"Yes, yes, same, same I am thinking."

At the last hospital on our tour, we had practically a state welcome. A long table was laid with a clean white table-cloth and silver dishes filled to the brim with nuts and fruit. We were garlanded. Rajmal, Kesari and I were ushered into three plastic chairs on one side of the table. Then no fewer than ten men took their seats opposite us.

"These are hospital trustees" explained Rajmal.

"Big hospital?" I asked.

Rajmal gave the closest resemblance to a smirk that such a restrained, polite man can muster.

Steaming cups of cardamom-flavoured tea were placed in front of us. Rajmal declined his, tea being part of the mango-apple-tea triad that he had given up in a pact with God in return for favours granted (usually associated with someone in the family recovering from an illness). However, the people in charge of serving us kept bringing in more tea. And each time that Rajmal declined his cup, I ended up drinking it. After five cups I was babbling.

Rajmal then informed me that most of the trustees could not understand any English anyway. He offered to translate.

Okay, so did the hospital have an ophthalmologist?

Only a part-time surgeon who came twice a week. He was paid a specific sum per operation.

Had Rajmal explained how Second Sight worked? Our surgeons were volunteers who offered their services to cure the blind.

Yes they understood this.

Did they want Second Sight surgeons?

Yes.

This particular hospital was fairly close to Jodhpur, a largish city with a reasonably well-off middle-class. The sight of ten reasonably well-off trustees reminded me of something. When we sent the first Second Sight surgeons to the Shree Bhairav, in spite of its location in a rural area, VIPs (as the richer patients are called) from the towns suddenly started turning up. They tried to push their way to the front of the queue to see the "foreign" doctor. Only Rajmal's firm stand that his hospital was first and foremost for the poor resulted in their waiting their turn like everyone else. I did not want the same thing to happen here.

Our aim was to reach the blind, I said. There were, after all, ten million of them out there. I told Rajmal to explain this but even my poor Hindi allowed me to realise that he talked to them about Second Sight's concern for "poor person" rather than for blind people.

And what a song and dance entailed. The trustee with the biggest paunch wanted to know what "poor" meant. Just because a man may looks dirty and wears rags, he was not necessarily poor, he said. Just because he, the trustee, was dressed in spotless white lungee and shirt did not mean that he was rich. He rested his case.

That was when I decided to ban the P word. Forever. Ahem.

"He's right," I said. "That is why we don't talk about the poor at all at Second Sight. We just talk about the blind. If you, sir, were blind, you should get your cataract operation free. And a Second Sight surgeon would be delighted to operate on you."

Rajmal translated and everyone smiled.

We sent volunteer surgeons to three charitable eye hospitals in rural Rajasthan. Rajmal was, however, very right in prophesying that the Second Sight relationship with each hospital would not be "same same."

At the Shree Bhairav the partnership achieved even more than we had hoped. Thousands more patients had their sight restored; visiting surgeons brought with them books, journals and teaching materials and a huge amount of clinical knowledge was exchanged with the resident doctors. Dr.Gulam Ali had a research paper accepted by the Royal College of Ophthalmologists in Britain. He and the other Bhairav eye surgeon Dr. Kaushlenra Kumar taught visiting Second Sight surgeons a cataract surgical technique that could be performed in five minutes. The British surgeons taught Gulam and Kaushlenra other kinds of ophthalmic surgery. Rajmal Jain even agreed for two ophthalmologists from a Christian missionary hospital, another of our partner hospitals, to undergo surgical training at the Shree Bhairav Hospital.

This was my dream coming true: a true partnership between British ophthalmologists and Indian ophthalmic teams; Indian hospitals helping each other regardless of religion, caste or class. What's more, the main criticism from larger charities that visiting surgeons were merely a "short-term" solution proved to be blatantly incorrect. It was integral to bringing about long-term benefits.

On my first visit in July 2000, Drs.Gulam Ali and Kaushlenra Kumar had both told me that they would not stay more than a year at the Bhairav Eye Hospital. In the end, they stayed eight and nine years respectively: the combination of the visiting surgeons providing a more stimulating working environment, Rajmal's cautious but intelligent raising of their salaries and the knowledge that people *as far away as Britain* respected them for their work was the magic formula that kept them working at a charitable hospital in the remote countryside.

Even when he left to go into private practise in the city of Jodhpur, close to his extended family, Dr.Gulam Ali took with him the ethos of the Bhairav Eye Hospital. He charges his patients the same reasonable rates that Rajmal asks from paying patients ("why ask people for too much money" he said). Gulam Ali is also now a volunteer Second Sight surgeon travelling to other parts of India to cure the blind.

The Shree Bhairav Eye Hospital now has no problem in recruiting experienced doctors who want to work there full-time. They have largely eradicated the backlog of people completely blind from cataract in that area of Rajasthan; the numbers of blind should never build up to monstrous proportions ever again.

What of the hospital with the ten trustees? Well, when Second Sight surgeons went there to work alongside the part-time Indian surgeon, they discovered that he was listing for cataract surgery pretty much everyone who walked through the hospital door! He was paid per operation, you see, so he wanted to keep his numbers up to maximise his income. He bullishly justified the unnecessary surgery by saying that as everyone develops cataract in the long run, taking out the natural lens and replacing it with a plastic lens *before* it developed cataract was doing them a service!

We informed the trustees and I also mentioned this to the international NGO that helped the hospital financially. No-one was interested. The records showed these patients had had cataract surgery and the numbers looked great on paper.

Just as Rajmal had predicted, not all hospitals were "same same." The same same can be said of charities.

PART TWO

Distracted by the Himalayas

Chapter Nine

In Rambo's Footsteps

Himachal Pradesh

The 16-seater Russian Dornier aircraft dropped down between the Himalayan foothills. We were so close to the scattered mountain-top homes I could make out the movements of people and animals. When a cloud wafted past partially obscuring the view I felt as if I could reach out and peel it away with ease. Then Bhuntar Airport's short runway became visible and we prepared for landing.

I had come to the state of Himachal Pradesh on account of a man called Rambo. Unlike the aggressive, gung-ho character portrayed by Sylvester Stallone in numerous films, this Rambo had been a gentle man. People who knew him talk of a tall, mild-mannered American eye surgeon who did more than any other individual to eradicate cataract blindness in rural north India during the 20th.century. He had died in the United States in 1987. I had heard that one of the few people trying to keep Dr.Rambo's legacy alive was an Indian man called Dennis Kendall. He ran a small cottage hospital in a village called Raison. I was there to meet him.

Dennis Kendall had been described to me as a "big fat fellow" by several people who had known him in his youth. So I was a bit taken aback when I first set eyes on the fairly trim, well-looking man who greeted me at the tiny airport at Kullu. He was wearing a Himachal pillar-box hat and a beautifully ironed shirt under a woollen cardigan, dark trousers and polished shoes. He could easily have been in his early sixties. He was then 72. Dennis is no longer a big fat fellow but he has a massive smile and a boundless commitment to the work he began with Victor Rambo.

We drove the 14kilometres from Kullu to Raison in an ancient jeep. It was driven by Deenu Ram, who turned out to be Dennis's right-hand man. As Deenu Ram negotiated the hair-pin bends and swore at lorries that tried to edge us off the narrow road, Dennis described his unexpected entry into the world of ophthalmology.

When he was 19years-old he had ended up in hospital in the city of Ludhiana in north India after a motorcycle accident. The legendary Dr.Rambo was the Professor of Ophthalmology at that time. He noticed the gloomy young man lying in bed with his broken limbs and approached him. He asked Dennis what plans he had for his future. Dennis was stumped. He had no plans. Dr.Rambo suggested that he dedicate his life to eye-care for India's poor. But I know nothing about eye-care, replied Dennis.

The next day Dr.Rambo turned up beside Dennis' hospital bed with a Vision Chart and taught him how easy it was to check a person's sight using it. Even without the chart you could gauge the level of sight by simply holding up your fingers and asking people to count them from a certain distance; the human finger is about the same size as the top letter on the chart.

Dennis was hooked. He became Dr.Rambo's disciple, went off for training in the United States and returned to work with him all over north India, including travelling by foot and by mule to provide mobile eye camps high up in the Himalayas.

"We carried everything with us," recalls Dennis. "Ophthalmic equipment, food, even a gramophone, because Dr.Rambo liked to listen to jazz and to dance. In fact, if patients were frightened before surgery, he would sometimes tap-dance to make the relatives laugh. Then everyone relaxed."

Dr.Rambo spent time heading the eye departments at India's two most well-known Christian Medical Colleges, at Ludhiana in the north and at Vellore in the south, institutions that were established to produce missionary doctors. He always emphasised, however, the importance of reaching the blind who lived then (just as they do now) in the rural areas. He described curing the blind as "the happiest work in the world". But, sadly, he failed to persuade any of his children, some of whom were doctors, to take over his missionary work when he retired. Sadly, too, said Dennis, the majority of graduates from the Christian medical colleges now end up abroad. Meanwhile, the backlog of people in India who are unnecessarily blind has been building. In Dr.Rambo's time there were about five million people blind from cataract; at the start of the 21st.century there was twice this number. Dennis and I agreed that poor Victor Rambo must be turning in his grave.

"But this place is still going" said Dennis, as we crossed the broad River Beas and turned right into the hospital gates. "I promised Dr.Rambo that I would never leave Raison."

Before us was a pretty patch of land, sloping up to a chalet-style house with a backdrop of snowy Himalayan peaks. Dennis told me that this was the guest-house. On the left was a tin-roofed shack with a large red cross painted on the side. This building had been the very first permanent structure at Raison Hospital, built with money donated by a grateful patient who had received treatment for a penetrating eye injury. It is still the Operating Theatre and Out-Patients Department. The building and three others constitute the entire hospital. As we walked slowly up the path, the tall trees muted the sound of traffic on the busy Kulu-Manali road; the loudest sound was the tinkle of bells worn by a few grazing cattle.

We sat on the verandah and a steady stream of patients began to come in. I noted that Dennis was quite able to deal with most common ophthalmic complaints, and was an experienced refractionist which meant that few people in this area would be walking around blind just for want of a pair of glasses. But what about the cataract blind? How often did an eye surgeon ever come to provide surgery?

Dennis explained that Raison Hospital was officially under India's National Programme for Control of Blindness, the NPCB in Delhi. But for years the NPCB had vacillated between occasionally sending eye surgeons to threatening to close the whole place down altogether. Only his friend, ophthalmologist Dr.Rajindra Trisal, was prepared to come once a month to clear some of the backlog of cases. A refugee from Kashmir, Dr.Trisal missed the mountains of his homeland so was happy to connect with the Himalayan range again. The only problem was that he was getting so busy with his work at a charitable hospital in Uttar Pradesh that the trips to Raison were becoming difficult. He was loathe to stop them though because each time he went there hundreds of patients converged on the cottage hospital and so many needed surgery that he operated until dropping from exhaustion. Reputation is everything when it comes to the poor trusting doctors in India, said Dennis. The kind of reputation that is built on good results not on impressive qualifications. If they were going to descend to the valleys from their mountain-homes, most people opted for the hospital they trusted most. In this case Raison.

We left the hospital grounds to take chai in the village and were almost mowed down by a fast-moving scooter with two people on it. The female passenger riding side-saddle with salwar kameez fluttering in the breeze beamed broadly and shouted out something in Hindi.

"That is Shakuntala" said Dennis. "She owns this tea stall."

A few moments later, Shakuntala and the speeding scooter were back. She skipped off and made her own introduction in Hindi. She was head of the village panchayat (local council) was 42years-old and had one daughter who had a medical problem (unspecified). She assisted in the operating theatre when Dr.Trisal came and liked nothing better.

Then, dropping her head and suddenly looking girlish as she looked up from under thick, dark lashes, she took my hand and asked me in English:

"Doc Sahib, you will teach me cataract surgery?"

If only. In some countries, for example in Africa, where there is a desperate shortage of surgeons, local paramedical staff are trained to do cataract operations. These schemes have been highly successful. In India, where there is no countrywide shortage of eye surgeons but a critical shortfall in the poorest areas, the medical establishment will fight tooth and nail to prevent paramedics from being trained specifically to tackle cataract blindness. Personally, I could not think of anything better than an intelligent leader of the community like Shakuntala being trained up to be a cataract surgeon. In addition, I suspected that Dennis already possessed the skills to carry out cataract surgery and had no doubt done so, unofficially, in Dr.Rambo's time. But we were in 21st.century India where the medical establishment behaves in a similar fashion to the medical establishment in Britain, fighting any move to encroach on a doctor's territory.

"Good assistants are as important as eye surgeons, Skakuntala," I said.

"You are sending eye surgeons to Raison Doc Sahib?" she asked enthusiastically.

Was I? The Big Boys in Delhi officially ran this hospital. Shouldn't I be trying to get them to send surgeons on a regular basis?

But then Dennis chimed in, in his slow, deliberate drawl that made everything sound so certain.

"Dr.Rambo told me that if I refused to leave this place, one day Raison would be a great hospital again. Now I think he is right. Doctor Lucy will send surgeons."

It seems we were committed. And as Dennis and Shakuntala were masters at organisation, the first Second Sight surgeon, Prasad Palimar, was at Raison, within months.

The camp was deemed to be a huge success. But the number of patients who had come with mature, blinding cataract was disappointingly low. Not because Dennis' formidable publicity machine had not brought them in, but simply because cataract blindness was not nearly as big a problem in Himachal as in Rajasthan. And, I was beginning to realise from my travels and my research, Rajasthan was not as badly off as rural areas of Uttar Pradesh, Bihar, Jharkhand and Orissa where millions were blind.

On the other hand, was I beginning to do what I had criticised other charities of doing: treating diseases rather than people, thinking about the impact on a 'problem' rather than the impact on each individual patient?

Our surgeon Prasad called at the end of the camp.

"You should have been here," he said hardly able to contain his mirth. "There was a big party, dancing, singing, good food. Then, you remember Thakur Sahib? The old chap who is on the hospital local management committee? Well he read out a lengthy valedictory poem that he had composed. You were the Angel of Light. And I was the Archangel Gabriel."

Thakur Sahib is a diminutive octogenarian, a retired local politician and friend of Dennis Kendall. He is a romantic. With an iron will.

Prasad further informed me that Thakur Sahib had announced to the world that the following summer Second Sight would be holding an eye camp thousands of feet higher up the Himalayas. We were to reach the people cut off from the rest of the world for six months of the year; we were to go into the moon-like landscape of Lahaul and Spiti and bring in the blind from remote villages bordering Tibet. This area just happened to be the location of Thakur Sahib's ancestral village.

I decided to defer any battle of wills with the determined Thakur Sahib. But it really was time to meet the group referred to by locals as the "people in Delhi": the National Programme for Control of Blindness.

Chapter Ten

Crisis? What crisis?

In the year 2002, I met a Professor of Ophthalmology in New Delhi, from India's National Programme for Control of Blindness. I had finally got around to arranging a meeting and had the perfect entry: the Second Sight surgeon who had done the Raison Eye Camp, Prasad Palimar, was a former colleague of the Professor and wanted me to pass on his best wishes on my next trip to Delhi. My real reason for meeting him was to pass on Dennis Kendall's concerns for the future of Raison and to ask why government ophthalmologists could not be sent there to provide cataract surgery for those who needed it. There was a pool of experienced doctors at the All India Institute for Medical Sciences in Delhi (AIIMS). Surely they could get some to operate at Raison on a regular basis. It was only an overnight bus journey away from the capital city.

The professor was late for our meeting. He had been summoned to the Ministry of Health. I was told this by his lugubrious male secretary who then spoke no further but began to type a report with the index finger of his right hand at the pace of a slow heart-beat.

When the professor did arrive he swept passed me straight into his office, giving me only a cursory glance, and the secretary indicated with a head movement that I should follow him.

I passed on good wishes from Prasad Palimar, the Second Sight surgeon whom he knew.

"It is good that you are sending people of Prasad's calibre," he said.

"But India doesn't have a blindness problem. Why don't Second Sight surgeons go to the Philippines instead?"

Given that at that time even the Government were quoting a figure of at least 10 million people blind from cataract in India, I gave the only appropriate response. I laughed.

"So those ten million people don't exist?" I asked.

Oh, he responded with an airy wave of the hand, Government schemes would get round to curing them all. They could easily be cured by the year 2020, the deadline set by the WHO for the eradication of reversible blindness throughout the world.

He was of course doing what most politicians do: claiming success well into the future (based on no evidence for such optimism) and using diversionary tactics to distract me from the problem at hand (his reference to the Philippines from where he had just returned on behalf of the Indian government).

"But professor wouldn't it be great to cure them all well *before* the 2020 deadline?" I asked.

"Yes, I am sure we will get there by the year 2015," he boomed confidently.

"We could all aim for 2010" I suggested.

"Sure" he replied. "India won't have a problem meeting any deadlines."

For some reason I began to feel I was in an absurd version of the game of Grandmother's Footsteps when you creep up on someone from behind but have to freeze like a statue when they turn around. If they catch you moving, you're out of the game. If you get to them without being caught moving, you win.

"But what if it were possible to cure them all by the year 2005?" I countered. And held my breath.

If this were Grandmother's Footsteps he chose not to turn around. So I continued.

"If your mother or my mother were blind from cataract we would not expect them to wait a single day, would we?"

The professor rose from his seat behind the desk. He had caught me moving. The game was over.

"Send me a proposal. I have another meeting."

We did not put in a proposal. I learned very rapidly that Indian ophthalmologists close to the corridors of power are not remotely concerned about blind people in the rural areas, and the eradication of cataract blindness in India is led not by them but by Non Governmental Organisations (NGOs).

However, I did put in a proposal, for funding, to our very own Government Department for International Development, DFID who are so vocal when it comes to meeting the United Nations Millennium Goals for reducing poverty. I did so because a retired friend and neighbour, who had worked for DFID for years, encouraged me to do so, even gave me a specific contact.

"What you are doing in rural India is amazing" he said."DFID should be giving you tons of money".

The rejection letter is still pinned to a board behind my desk.

DFID was unable to consider funding because "your work is about the provision of health-care and not empowerment."

He explained that DFID preferred to support schemes that helped the poor to "understand why" they were caught in the poverty trap, schemes that would "empower" them to change their situation.

I promptly wrote back saying that in many areas the cataract blind were not blind through ignorance : these days, even in the most remote areas in which we worked, I had found that people were well aware of what a cataract was and that there was an operation to cure the blindness it caused.

"Safed moti" or white pearl is the Hindi term for cataract because that is what it looks like: when a mature cataract is so dense that it causes complete blindness, the whole pupil looks white instead of black. Illiterate villagers can make the diagnosis. But they cannot come for surgery if the family is too poor to allow another member to take a day off work, if they cannot afford the travel expenses, or if they have to pay for the surgery.

Surely the best way to empower a blind person was to restore their sight? I asked DFID.

Treating me like a recalcitrant child their next letter asked if I would like some advice about re-applying in the future.

So here are the facts: cataract surgery has been listed amongst the Ten Best Health Interventions to Reduce Poverty; possibly the most cost-effective surgery known to Medicine, it can restore sight in less than ten minutes. But, oh dear, is this really empowering poor people?

Clearly Government spokespeople both at home and in India were not in the habit of actually consulting the poor, the disempowered or the blind. This made it even more important that we would never fall into the trap of making 'desk' decisions in favour of humane ones. Which meant of course that we had to return to the Himalayas.

Chapter Eleven

Thakur Sahib's Triumph

Himachal Pradesh

I wouldn't call Chief Medical Officer Dr.Cherring an assertive man. But he definitely meant business when he looked me straight in the eye and said "Doc Sahib, you can go and publicise the eye camp in the villages, but you MUST be back here by 2pm. The MLA (the local MP) is coming and you are the Chief Guest."

Then, perhaps in case I refused, he added:

"Thakur Sahib will go with you."

84year-old Thakur Sahib drew himself up to his full five feet, expanded his chest and patted the medals that hung from the pocket of his light, grey pin-striped suit. A colourful Himachal pillar-box hat, red and yellow, matched the silk scarf round his throat. His light, watery eyes smiled through the gold-framed spectacles. He was as pleased as punch. Not only were we there to organise the eye camp that he had predicted would take place, but I, the "very famous Founder of Second Sight" had been asked to be the Chief Guest at a big function. What's more he, Thakur Sahib had been involved in every step of the process. This was all going to make such good material for the memoirs he was currently putting together. So far he had written about the Old Days, when the 'Paks' (Pakistanis) had made forays over the border with India and had killed "our boys". The then Prime Minister of India, Pandit Nehru, was, according to Thakur Sahib, at a loss as to how to get Indian troops up into the mountains to stop this pillage.

"I said to Nehru. Use the mountain trails. We can show you where they are."

With the same pride Thakur Sahib guided us through the area known as Lahaul and Spiti deciding where we would stop and drink mint tea with the locals and giving us a potted history of every Buddhist temple that we passed.

For at least six months of the year Lahaul and Spiti is cut off from the rest of the world, walled in by snow and ice. In the warm months it is gorgeous: a terrain of verdant slopes and bubbling streams and all the flowers from a British country garden reaching for the skies, growing Masai-tall in their brief growth-spurt.

Thakur Sahib arranged for us to stay at Keylong Circuit House, Government accommodation usually kept for visiting officials from other states in India. It was a beautiful setting, in its own well-kept garden and with Himalayas stretched out on all sides. Thakur Sahib insisted that they gave me the room at the end of the veranda.

"Prime Minister Indira Gandhi always stayed in that room" he told me. "You will be sleeping in Mrs. Gandhi's bed. That will bring you luck."

As Indira Gandhi had been assassinated I was not at all sure about this. But I was beginning to think that telling people they were lucky was a kind of Himalayan compliment. At Key Monastery, a young, permanently beaming monk also told me I was lucky: I was publicising the camp at the time of the Full Moon; even better, the Dalai Lama was due to visit the area at the same time as the camp. Perhaps his Holiness might want to come and bless some blind patients, I enquired. Still smiling he replied that the Dalai Lama's schedule was intense so this was not possible. But he and his fellow monks would spread the word about the eye camp.

When we returned to Keylong Hospital for the function at which I was to be Chief Guest, the place was awash with people ranked around a huge circular conference table with microphones, and colourful banners decorated the walls.

"Keylong Hospital Celebrates the Launch of Family Awareness Week" they proclaimed. It turned out to be the start of the Anti-Aids Campaign by the Health Department of Lahaul and Spiti.

The guests were all individually welcomed, pretty pillar-box Himachel hats placed on our heads and garlands draped around our necks.

Then Dr.Cherring launched the campaign by announcing that Lahaul and Spiti had yet to record *a single case* of a person who was HIV positive. A lot of clapping greeted this and delicious roasted cashew nuts and sweet hot tea were handed round. I suppose I should have continued in the celebratory mood but I couldn't help myself. When it was my turn to speak at the microphone, I told them that there might not be any Aids in Lahaul and Spiti but there were 200 people who had been identified as being *blind* from cataract! An experienced visiting eye surgeon was coming who could cure them all during the upcoming eye camp. But this relied on the local team bringing the patients to hospital.

Perhaps something was lost in translation because I did not get much of a response, particularly considering I was the honoured Chief Guest. The kind-faced politician, the MLA smiled and intimated that he would like to say something.

Dr. Lucy was talking about a "cataract free zone" he told them. And the place erupted. Silly me, I was forgetting that in India audiences have grown to expect slogans so throwing out a catch-phrase is often the easiest way to enthuse a crowd. Still refusing to play the game entirely, however, I whispered to the MLA that it would be a "cataract *blindness* free zone"; people would always develop cataract but the unnecessary blindness caused by allowing this condition to go untreated was the problem.

"That is technicality" he replied, as one of his aides pushed another plate of cashews towards me.

I caught the eye of a man sitting opposite with his hat perched at a jaunty angle. He smiled and wobbled his head as if he understood my frustration. Then he seized his microphone and announced: "The benefits of washing in cow's urine cannot be overestimated."

They paid him about as much attention as they had paid me.

Perhaps I should have taken this as an omen for we did not make Lahaul and Spiti a "cataract blindness free zone." In spite of the fact that the Government District Hospital had thirty health workers and eight junior doctors, in spite of their detailed knowledge of exactly where each blind person lived, during two eye camps only 100 patients were brought in for cataract surgery. But hundreds more came of their own accord with minor ophthalmic complaints or for glasses so Dennis was kept busy. Our Second Sight surgeon Dr.Gulam Ali, who had travelled from Rajasthan to operate, was severely under-used...although not exactly unhappy as the mountains were a pleasant change from the Rajasthan summer heat.

Once again, I was at the end of a phone hearing about the camps, having returned to work in Britain after the publicity campaign. I did my best to persuade, cajole, bully Dr.Cheering, Thakur Sahib, everybody, to go out and get the blind, not to waste this opportunity of having a skilled eye surgeon there to operate. It didn't work. The locals remained surprised at my annoyance and, in frequent phone-calls and with almost irritatingly consistent good humour, tried to get me to relax, lavishing me with thanks and compliments.

Only Dennis knew the way to stop me complaining.

"You remember that little boy" he said in his slow drawl. "The one we met on the road with his father. Both had broken glasses."

I remembered. Ten year-old Angu had been born with cataract and his parents had travelled over 1,000 kilometres with him when he was a toddler to a hospital outside Delhi. The cataracts were removed but intra-ocular lenses were not placed within the eye (this was common then with paediatric cases). Instead Angu had been fitted with glasses that allowed him to see well. Without the glasses he could not see. When we met him, on a mountain trail during the publicity campaign, both Angu and his father were wearing glasses that were held together by tape and string. Dennis had told them to come to the Second Sight eye camp for examination and to be issued with new glasses.

"They came to the camp " said Dennis. "Now they are happy. Both have new spectacles."

In the end we did decide to pull out of the Himalayas. I discovered that there are many foreign groups ready to go and do eye camps in this beautiful part of the world. Also, the NPCB suddenly started to pay Raison Hospital some attention. I like to think we may have influenced them. Now, they send eye surgeons from Delhi to operate every month throughout the spring and summer.

Of course Dennis and Thakur Sahib continue to tell me that the Second Sight eye camps were the best. And one year, during the harsh Himachal winter I received a phone-call from Dr.Cherring, the medical officer at Keylong. He was with a group of health workers and they were having a few drinks.

"We are all missing you Doc Sahib" he announced mournfully, as if I had lived there all my life. "All are begging you to return."

The sound quality was bad but I could visualise the scene : men and women in layered clothing huddled together in a smoky shack, reminiscing for hours on end, wide-eyed children at their feet. I could practically smell the wood-fires over the mobile phone connection…not to mention the liquor that was obviously being consumed in great quantities.

"Doc Sahib(hic)…can you call back…phone credit is low…"

Not a chance. I had fallen for those charming Himalayan manners on too many occasions. It was time to follow Dr.Rambo's footprints into less enchanting territory.

PART THREE

On the missionary trail

Chapter Twelve

Light of Life

Uttar Pradesh

My mother, who was brought up in south India by strict Catholic nuns, either Irish or French, is full of praise for the schooling she had from missionaries and for most of the philosophy they imparted to her. That is why my second name is Celine, in memory of a French nun with a beautiful voice and gutsy manner. Other Indians from that generation, however, feel less kindly towards Christian missionaries. There may express adulation for Dr.Rambo but criticism of other Christian doctors rumoured to have applied pressure on patients to convert to Christianity in return for medical treatment.

In modern India it would be foolish for any Christian group to be so fanatical and I have never come across a hospital that worked in this way; Christians are already easy targets for religious militants from other faiths and, indeed, from bullies of all kinds.

The fact is that even now, in 21st. century India, there are huge swathes of the rural north where there are no government hospitals that patients trust, sometimes no hospitals at all. And in these areas, the mission hospitals are all there are.

Three years into the work of Second Sight, the lack of eye surgeons in these areas was still the main reason for the blind remaining blind. So it was imperative to check out as many Christian mission hospitals that I could find.

First stop on my missionary trail was the Christian Hospital at Roberstganj in the state of Uttar Pradesh. I had heard about it from the ophthalmologist who had set up the Eye Department there; we had worked together in Surrey.

The Robertsganj hospital, called the Jiwan Jyoti—Light of Life-- can be reached by a long train journey from Delhi to the Hindu's holiest city Varanasi and then by a three hour journey by road.

I was picked up by a burley driver with a tattoo on the muscles of his right arm: a large cross and Jesus Loves You written underneath. He was very sweet but spoke only a little English. With him was another Jiwan Jyoti employee, occupation unclear, who spoke excellent English. He was very serious.

We negotiated our way through the teeming narrow lanes of the ancient city, past the famous Hindu University and the German bakeries. The vehicle scraped past cycle-rickshaws laden with tiny, neatly uniformed schoolchildren, or Muslim women in hajibas, or inanimate objects like enormous freezers or massive mirrors. Once or twice a water buffalo blocked our path and headed straight for us with that determined refusal to give way that these creatures have. Then the roads widened and cars became predominant and the incessant blaring of horns seared the air. As we swung past a roundabout a small naked child with a pot-belly tottered in the middle of the road. The vehicles manoeuvred around her, none stopping.

I sat in the front of the jeep with both the Jiwan Jyoti employees. The back was full of equipment and food that they had picked up in Varanasi and were transporting back to the hospital. On the dashboard there was a paperback entitled "Doctors who have found God". The serious chap kept pushing this across the dashboard in my direction. The bends on the road conspired to push the book back towards him.

We stopped for lunch. I was tucking into my biriani before I noticed the awkward looks and the fact that no-one else had started eating. Shall we pray? said the serious one. I muttered apologies. I have worked with so many Christians in India now that I would not dream of forgetting to allow someone to say Grace before eating, but the punctuation of every action with prayer was new to me then.

When we resumed our jeep-journey, he asked me why I had started Second Sight, what had motivated me. Being an ophthalmologist and knowing that people were unnecessarily blind, I replied. Yes, but what *really* motivated you? What fuelled your enthusiasm for this work? Of course I knew what he was getting at: he wanted me to say that God motivated me. I resolutely refused to introduce God into the conversation.

The Jiwan Jyoti is the only charitable hospital that serves a large area of rural UP, but the hospital itself is on a busy main road in a town. As we swung in through the iron gates, families of patients were cooking meals on small fires in the courtyard and the hospital's then CEO, Mr.Jone Wills, was chatting to them.

After the mildly antagonistic atmosphere in the jeep, it was a profound relief to meet Jone Wills. In spite of being rather overweight and short of breath Jone has tremendous energy and is a wonderfully warm, friendly and passionate man.

He had already done his research on me: discovered from the internet that I had been a journalist and was now an ophthalmologist. He knew all about Second Sight's modus operandi: providing volunteer surgeons for hospitals on condition that the hospitals specifically targeted those who were blind. He said that even with two resident eye surgeons the Jiwan Jyoti had a waiting list of patients desperate for sight-restoring surgery.

He took me on a guided tour of the hospital, taking his time to talk to patients and translate their stories to me. In the Obstetrics department a 20year-old was screaming her way through a difficult labour. Jone sort out her relatives in the ward next-door and we spent half an hour talking to them. The mother-in-law told me that she had had seven children but she was determined that her daughter and daughter-in-law would have only two. She knew that pregnant women needed a good diet just to survive. But how could this happen when there were so many mouths to feed. You know all this, because you are an educated woman, she told me. We learn only when we come to places like this.

"Dr.Lucy, you know forty per cent of women who come here to deliver are so severely anaemic that they need blood transfusions," said Jone. "But we have no blood bank. Sometimes relatives give blood. Sometimes there is nothing we can do. So people die."

We moved on to the Premature Babies Unit where tiny brown babies, two to an incubator, determinedly fought to get a hold on life, overlooked by posters of podgy white babies with drooling smiles.

We eventually got to the Eye Department and in a cramped room found ophthalmologist Dr. Subodh Rath surrounded by patients. There were diagrams on the wall of different parts of the eye, just as in our own NHS eye clinics. Few patients paid them any attention. However, they were showing interest in a Snakes and Ladders poster on one wall. When I looked more closely, I saw that the game was being used to educate the patients about what to do and not do after cataract surgery: rub your eye and you slid down a snake, come for your follow-up appointment and you whizzed up a ladder.

"Actually this is a Government poster" said Jone Wills. "One of the few useful things the Government has done. Snakes and Ladders is a popular game in this part of the world. It is a very good way to educate illiterate patients about post-operative eye-care."

The atmosphere of the hospital was great; staff were run off their feet but cheerful. I was worried, however, about the cramped conditions and lack of space for expansion. If Second Sight surgeons came here the in-patient load would go up phenomenally overnight. Would they be able to cope? Where would they put all the extra patients?

"Yes we can cope," said Jone "Send your surgeons in the four busy winter months. We will use all the wards and any extra space we find. After all, if we have the opportunity to restore sight to so many more poor people, we must do it."

Then he added: "If we run out of space, we can even use the Church. What do you think Subodh?"

Dr.Subodh looked a little concerned about the proposal.

"I think that there are some people who might not like that" he commented quietly. (Yes, like the serious chap who picked me up from the station). But I was loving this practical Christianity emanating from the CEO. If the Church was central to their belief then it should also be at the centre of the work.

I saw an example of this the next morning. After the usual prayer meeting, the doctors gathered at the back of the church for a ward round and interesting or difficult cases that had presented overnight were discussed. This was a great way to keep in touch with other specialties and to build team spirit. It was also when I learned that ophthalmologist Dr.Subodh had been on-call for the entire hospital overnight and had carried out two caesarean sections! Goodness, was this what they expected of us? There was a terrifying moment when I pictured the Jiwan Jyoti nursing team looking expectantly at a visiting Second Sight surgeon as a woman in a complicated labour screamed for attention.

"Jone, our visiting ophthalmologists won't be doing any caesarean sections" I said as firmly as I could.

"Oh don't worry," he said. "Dr. Subodh is an old-fashioned missionary doctor. He can turn his hand to any emergency. The new generation are like doctors from the UK. We won't expect this from Second Sight surgeons."

Phew.

Having cleared this matter up I agreed that I would send the first eye surgeons in time for the busy winter months. Jone Wills looked pleased.

"There are plenty of mission hospitals that could do with this kind of help," he said.

"Then point me in their direction" I replied.

Chapter Thirteen

Doctor Helen's Eye

"Don't worry madam, I am seeing everything."

Oh yee of little faith. Just because I, with my 20/20 vision, was able to see absolutely zero through the dense fog completely surrounding the scooter-rickshaw this did not mean that the driver did not possess super-powers. He was certainly behaving as if he could indeed see "everything" as he drove the converted scooter straight on, fairly fast, from my guest-house to the railway station.

He looked a disconcertingly ghostly figure viewed from the passenger-seat, his woollen shawl draped over head and shoulders, but he tried to reassure me of his good intentions by frequently turning round to smile.

There was little other traffic on the road, one supposed not just on account of the fog but because it was hardly 5am on a cold January morning in New Delhi.

Just when I thought that matters could not get much scarier, the familiar spluttering of the scooter engine stopped, and we were stationary.

"No problem madam. I can start."

He leapt out of the rickshaw, raised the top of the driver's seat and yanked at something. I waited patiently.

Two large lights appeared through the fog. A huge lumbering form was heading for us. The scooter-rickshaw driver paid it no attention.

As the form drew nearer, an ominous cigar-shaped object projected from it, pointing directly at us.

The shape of a human being detached itself from the large lumbering object and landed beside the rickshaw. A turbaned head appeared a few inches from my face, a stiff hand held in a salute by the eyebrows. The face smiled broadly.

"Good morning, madam" said the Sikh soldier.

"Indian army. Republic Day parade practise. No need for alarm."

The scooter rickshaw spluttered into life and we drove past a line of hundreds of Indian army tanks and good-humoured soldiers. I felt as if I was inspecting a guard of honour.

The first half of that particular trip to India was totally dominated by the fog. Every train I took was delayed hours. I grew used to seeing the world in a gloom, felt as if I were in a dream because sounds, too, seemed to be affected by the fog, becoming muffled and ambiguous. When a journey dragged out too much, I resorted to listening to music on my walkman. The album Absolution by the band Muse only added to the surrealism: the falsetto voice of lead singer Matthew Bellamy sang apocalyptic lyrics into my ears while before my eyes bare-footed, hooded people huddled around wood fires on station platforms or stood shivering at tea-stalls, featureless in the fog.

A trip to Bihar, India's notorious "kidnap state" was on my schedule. I was thankful that I would have with me a companion, an old school friend Angie Gleeson, a first-timer in India but someone guaranteed to see the best side of any situation.

We boarded the Delhi-Raxaul train and installed ourselves in the Air-conditioned two-tier sleeper class. Armed guards walked slowly through the carriages, rifles slung casually round their shoulders.

I have travelled through Bihar so many times since, by road and by rail, and so have many different people associated with Second Sight, both surgeons and non-surgeons. None of us has had any trouble whatsoever. Some of us now feel more at home in rural Bihar than in Delhi or Kolkata. That first trip for me was so different from all consequent visits that one must conclude that the state's Bad Press, our own preconceptions, and perhaps the eeriness of the thick fog, conspired to present Bihar as a Dickensian nightmare.

Train 4015 was delayed 22 hours. This was, we were told by fellow passengers, because people were pulling the emergency cord when the train approached their villages so that they could jump off. We wondered how on earth they could tell where their villages were in the dense fog but perhaps that was part of the problem: oops wrong place, have to pull that cord again later. Each time the cord was pulled, the poor old train driver stopped and the armed guards took a cursory tour around the carriages. No-one showed the slightest frustration.

At 4am, we pulled into Raxaul station. For some reason, the platform was such a distance below the bottom step of the carriage that we had to jump down. I nearly jumped onto a small cloth parcel. The cloth parcel turned out to be a small human being. The entire platform was covered by small human beings, asleep beneath their coverings, so tiny it was as if we had landed in the land of Gulliver's Lilliputians. The fog was as dense as ever.

We made our way to the exit. Outside was a white van. "The Duncan Christian Hospital" said the sign on the side. We knocked on a window and roused a bleary-eyed driver. Half an hour later we were at The Duncan Hospital guest-house and fast asleep in our beds.

The next morning there was brilliant winter sunshine. Not a trace of the fog that had dogged us for so long. We headed for the Eye Department to meet Dr.Helen Nirmala Rao, the ophthalmologist in charge. A sign, a huge painted eye loomed over the entrance to the building, a friendly eye that most definitely offered a welcome. And out of the building emerged a woman in a bright green sari, with black hair disappearing down her back in one thick plait that almost reached her feet.

"So happy that you have arrived safely" she said. Then gesturing upwards to the sign she added: "The patients call this Dr.Helen's Eye. And I am Dr.Helen."

That was the beginning of the Second Sight love affair with the much-maligned state of Bihar. And that has much to do with the personality and charisma of Dr.Helen who has dedicated her entire working life to a forgotten corner of India and transformed the lives of thousands of India's blind people.

Standing under "Dr.Helen's Eye" there was a feeling of having come home. I was at last in the heart of Bihar, where the greatest number of India's blind people lived. Eye patients were streaming up the ramp to the self-contained building that was the Ophthalmology Department and were being dealt with in an orderly fashion by courteous staff. Others milled around us raising their hands in Namaste or approaching Dr.Helen to ask questions. She gave each patient or relative her complete concentration breaking off from her conversation with us to give them precedence.

We had travelled a thousand kilometres across the breadth of north India, from Rajasthan to the Indo-Nepalese border in Bihar. Yet Rajmal Jain's Bhairav Eye Hospital at Bisalpur and Helen Rao's eye department at Raxaul felt reassuringly similar.

Chapter Fourteen

Two grains in the palm of a hand

The hymns were sung in Hindi and were not recognizable tunes so we couldn't join in. There was no need to worry though as Dr.Helen's nurses sang so strongly the sound filled the corridor. The Hindu patients, already dressed for the operating theatre in smocks and paper caps, sat almost motionless, some displaying mildly curious expressions. Most of them couldn't see the white-coated members of staff standing before them. They probably assumed that the singing was a necessary prelude to their operations. Which in a way it was at this Christian missionary outpost in north-western Bihar.

Singing over, it was down to business.

"Come, Angie," said Dr.Helen to my friend Angela Gleeson, whom she had already co-opted as her non-medical assistant. "Lucy has seen many cases like this but you will not have seen before."

She moved towards the patients and gently lifted the chin of an elderly woman so that she could shine a torch into her right eye.

"This patient went to some village quack for the left eye. It got some infection. That eye is useless. Now she has mature cataract in the right eye. We can remove that for her and she will see again."

The next patient was a youngish man, white cataracts in both eyes.

"This man has a small shop. His family brought him in because it seems he was behaving in an odd way. They thought he had some mental problem. Actually, he was losing his sight. He could not serve his customers and count the money. This was making him very anxious. As you can see, he is blind from cataract in both eyes."

As soon as we began to work in Bihar we saw that the cataract blindness problem had probably been underestimated there. Figures for blindness were most often based on surveys of people over the age of fifty. But in Bihar we were seeing so many much younger patients completely blinded by mature cataract.

Worldwide the main risk factor for developing cataract is age. But cataract is six times more common in a typical, developing tropical country like India, compared with a developed country with a temperate climate like Britain. People argue about the precise causes for this but solar radiation and severe dehydration are the most popular theories. A child suffering from repeated episodes of gastroenteritis or acute fever can end up as a young adult with blinding cataract. As John Sandford Smith wrote in his excellent book "Eye Diseases in Hot Climates"

"The health of the lens seems to be a very good indication of the general health of the body."

No surprise then that India's poorest state harbours so many people blinded by cataract.

And that is what brought Dr.Helen Nirmala Rao to Bihar. She and her husband, Anand, a general surgeon, are originally from the south Indian state of Andhra Pradesh. When they first arrived at the messy, chaotic town of Raxaul on the Indo-Nepalese border, they did not like it at all. But they saw the desperate need of patients coming to the hospital and decided to spend their working life there.

Helen was a physician for eight years at Raxaul until one day she opened the Bible and read this passage:

"I, the LORD, have called you in righteousness; I will take hold of your hand. I will keep you and will make you to be a covenant for the people and a light for the Gentiles,

  to open eyes that are blind,"

Helen took this as a message from God that she should train as an eye surgeon. She returned to south India to train at the reputable Trichy Eye Hospital in Tamil Nadu. Then she went back to Raxaul and built up the Ophthalmology Department from scratch. For many years she carried out all the surgery herself, up to 2,000 operations a year. This took its toll. Too much time bent over microscopes and slit-lamps in appalling posture brought on neck problems. Pain had now almost put a complete stop to her surgery. But she still continued all other ophthalmic work. A junior surgeon joined Helen's department to operate so the department never stopped providing cataract operations. But the work-load was seriously reduced.

We had made the journey to Raxaul at the suggestion of Jone Wills, the CEO of the Jiwan Jyoti Christian Hospital to which we were by then sending regular rotas of surgeons for nine months of the year. Both hospitals were run by the same huge Christian organisation. If Dr.Helen was no longer able to do much operating perhaps Second Sight surgeons could step in to help. Having seen the Jiwan Jyoti flourish since the Second Sight partnership, Jone wanted the same for Dr.Helen's department.

By the time I met Helen, I had already been made aware of the difficulties faced by charitable hospitals in rural north India. India's National Programme for Control of Blindness (NPCB) has money available for any NGO hospital that is tackling the blindness problem. A hospital can receive 750 rupees for each cataract operation it carries out if it supplies the correct surgical data and other paperwork. I have seen the paperwork and it is not that tedious to fill in. The system works well in most of south India.

However, corruption and incompetence in the state of Bihar means that the NPCB money rarely reaches the right hospitals. After eight years of applications for this money, Dr.Helen had given up applying. Her eye department, by the way, was at that time, the only place where poor patients could go in two huge districts of Bihar.

As if this wasn't enough, Dr.Helen was also facing problems from her own management. I could empathise with this. Our own NHS in Britain was becoming increasingly manager-dominated. The difference was that a conflict of view-points in a remote rural hospital in India can be devastating for patients.

One particular day brought this home to me in a very stark manner. Helen and I were examining patients in clinic. Towards the end of the morning a woman called Lalpari Devi walked in.

She was stick-thin, which made her large neck goitre look all the more monstrous. She told her story with many elegant hand gestures and occasionally fiddled with the patch over her left eye. She was 35years-old but looked fifty. Her husband squatted on the floor beside her chair and added to the tale. They owed the hospital 50 rupees.

Dr. Helen listened carefully, consulted the hospital card, wrote "Account Settled" in red letters and told them to take the card to the hospital cashier. But first she removed the eye patch to examine the eye which had been operated on two weeks before for a mature cataract. Lalpari Devi smiled.

We saw some more patients before being interrupted by a quiet tap on the door. Lalpari Devi and her husband had returned. The cashier still insisted that they had to pay 50 rupees. Dr. Helen assured them that they did not and told them to go back. They returned again. They had now been told that if they wanted the dark protective glasses issued to post-operative eye patients, they would have to pay 100 rupees. Dr. Helen wrote "issue spectacles" on the card. They returned a final time, to say goodbye, with broad smiles. It was easy to share in their happiness: not only had Lalpari Devi got her sight back, but they had questioned the system and had won.

This was the background to their story. Lalpari Devi and her husband had originally come to the hospital when Dr.Helen had been away. She had lost all vision in her left eye and could only make out hand movements with her right eye. She was told she had cataract and that she would have to pay 500 rupees for an operation. They could not afford this so they went back to their village.

Their second visit to the hospital was made when Lapari's left eye became painful. She had developed glaucoma (high pressure in the eye caused by leakage of material from the mature cataract). The hospital said that of course they would treat her but she must find some money to pay for the cataract operation. Her husband went to everyone he knew and scraped together 450 rupees.

It was only when Helen and I saw Lalpari Devi in clinic that the whole story came out. Helen was furious. She told me that her staff were under continuous pressure to charge patients, even when the administrators knew that this would mean turning away the poorest who were inevitably blind, and taking only better-off patients with early cataract who could still see well.

"Our administrators are always talking about money," she said. "But while they are enjoying biscuits with their tea, we are supposed to charge poor patients. This is not right for a mission hospital."

Later that day, the Head of Ophthalmology for the entire hospital chain arrived at Raxaul, a short man with a domineering manner. He summoned all the outreach workers. He singled out one male worker.

If his mother needed a cataract operation wouldn't he find 500 rupees to pay for her operation, the Head of Ophthalmology asked?

Well, yes, replied the cowed worker. But he was lucky that he could come up with that sum of money; when he went into the villages he saw many people who simply could not afford this fee.

"Chup!" replied his boss, holding up his hand in a commanding manner to silence the worker. It was their duty to ensure that all patients paid. A flat fee of 500 rupees was affordable by all.

I later challenged this fellow ophthalmologist over the case of Lalpari Devi. I pointed out that turning her away from a simple cataract operation had not just left her blind but had resulted in her re-presenting at the hospital as an emergency: with a painful blind eye directly brought about by the delay in her cataract operation. He confabulated and said that of course they were exceptions to the rules about payment and that this should not have happened. But he was adamant about the principle: most people could pay.

I explained that Second Sight did not believe in blind patients paying for their operation. It would be pointless to provide eye surgeons to cure the blind and then see poverty keeping patients from coming into hospital for the surgery. Oh, if Second Sight wanted to pay for the operations that was fine, he replied without hesitation.

It was very tempting to point out the inconsistency of his professed belief that all patients could afford 500 rupees and his ready acceptance of Second Sight money. But I didn't. The important outcome of the meeting was to ensure that there would be no more unfortunate cases like that of Lalpari Devi.

So we sent one surgeon after the other to Dr.Helen's department at Raxaul. Patients poured in because of their trust in both her and a team which now included a Second Sight surgeon for almost every month of every year.

It became the favourite eye department for volunteers. Perhaps because it was impossible not to get thoroughly immersed in the lives of patients. Eye surgeon Jenny Watts went there every February up till 2009 and each time returned with stories that captivated her patients back in Britain. One tale is encapsulated on the Second Sight Calendar of 2005 in a photograph taken by Jenny.

The picture shows Helen with her back to the camera facing a family of five. The oldest child, his head framed by a maroon woollen balaclava is smiling straight at the camera and clapping his hands. A toddler, also wearing the same woollen head-gear, peers shyly from behind his brother's leg. The mother, a young woman, is giving all her attention to the baby in her lap who is swaddled in layers of clothing and has coal-rimmed eyes. The father stands behind them. Even though the top of his head is cut off in the photo you can see that he, too, is smiling.

Everyone was happy because the mother,Chalu Devi, was seeing her newest baby for the first time. She had been blind from cataract but had operations on both eyes carried out by Jenny Watts.

"So there was everybody drooling over the baby," Jenny told me. "And then the husband stepped forward and stood in front of his wife. His fist was clenched. He unclenched the fist and there in the palm of his hand were two grains, one of rice and one of wheat. His main concern was that she could now see well enough to distinguish between the two and presumably return to her cooking duties!"

Chapter Fifteen

Money matters

For the first few years of Second Sight we ran on a very low income, our main input to the eradication of blindness programme in India being the provision of experienced eye surgeons. As all these surgeons were volunteers and the hospitals provided food and accommodation we only needed money for travel expenses. And British Airways played their part in helping to keep the cost of airfares down.

Then two things happened. We went into partnership with Christian mission hospitals who could not afford to pay for the extra surgery; and our surgeons got faster and faster at their work! The latter was fantastic and as a result of their returning over and over again to the same hospitals and the entire ophthalmic teams getting more efficient. The former was just something we had to deal with. By paying for the surgery. I stepped up the number of letters I wrote to small grant-giving organisations and a growing band of volunteers (eye surgeons, their families and many non-medical friends) used their initiative to raise more money.

Nevertheless, there was always the unexpected.

Right in the middle of the busiest month for operating, the patient transportation vehicle at the Jiwan Jyoti Hospital at Robertsganj broke down. It was a 10year-old bus. Meanwhile, hundreds of patients were waiting for collection in outlying villages. Jone Wills was on the phone to me straight away. Never one to beat about the bush, he announced:

"We can hire vehicles to bring them in, but it is costing quite a bit of money. Would Second Sight be able to help out?"

While I had been at the Jiwan Jyoti I had inspected the old bus and seen that it was on its last legs. It had been donated by a large international charity. Dr.Subodh and I wrote an application to this charity for a replacement vehicle. He informed me that, if the application was approved, it would still take at least a year for the vehicle to be with them.

I spoke to my trustees. What was the use of sending eye surgeons if the patients could not get to hospital? I asked. If there were blind patients and Second Sight surgeons available to cure them, then nothing should stop that happening. Now we had to put our money where our mouth was.

"That's all fine" said my businesswoman-sister-trustee Sue Lownds. "But are you prepared to continue to step into emergency situations like this? It's going to happen again and again. And it's you who will have to find the extra money."

"I can do that. There's no choice," I said with bravado.

I had spent the last few months chasing one of Britain's richest Indian-born residents, steel baron Laksmi Mittal. Or to be more accurate, his wife Usha. I had got as far as speaking to her on the phone and thought I sensed some, mild, interest in our work. She said that her daughter was interested in getting involved in humanitarian projects. I had told her about Jone Wills at Robertsganj and learned that she had relatives in the area. She had asked for the hospital telephone number and actually made a call. Jone reports a friendly conversation and agreement that the Mittal relatives would visit the Jiwan Jyoti. Then nothing happened. In addition, an agreed meeting between her, myself and Second Sight surgeon Srinivasan Subramaniam, was cancelled. Calling from her then home in Millionaire's Row in London's Hampstead area, Usha Mittal said that she had spoken to her husband and he had said that they were already "doing a lot of charitable work."

At about the same time that Jone was ringing me about the broken down bus, there was a lot in the Press about the impending marriage of the Mittals' daughter. The event was rumoured to be running up a bill of over £30million.

I decided that some brinkmanship was called for. We had nothing to lose.

I wrote an email to Usha Mittal.

Dear Usha Mittal,

I know that your daughter is interested in the eradication of blindness in India. I also know that she is getting married soon. A Second Sight surgeon also recently got married and included on her Gifts' List the option for family and friends to donate to Second Sight! £10,000 can so easily be spent on just part of a day's celebration. It could also restore sight to thousands of blind people and change their lives and the lives of those who help them, forever.

Best wishes

Dr.Lucy Mathen

Usha Mittal donated the money. The Jiwan Jyoti got their bus and did not have to turn away the blind. Sadly, the bus crashed two years later, badly injuring the driver and killing one elderly woman. Survivors had their cataract operations. The crushed vehicle stood in the Jiwan Jyoti grounds for weeks, the inscription "Donated by Savitri Dalmia" partially visible. In spite of appeals, Usha Mittal chose not to replace the bus she had donated in memory of her mother. I am grateful to her, though. At least she had donated money to us, a low-profile charity, and in response to a personal appeal. And that is as rare as hen's teeth amongst the super-rich.

The Jiwan Jyoti bus incident brought Money to the forefront of my thoughts. As, of course, my trustee-sister had intended. There was little doubt that our expenditure was going to increase rapidly. As an entirely volunteer-run organisation, could we continue to raise enough? Bits of money were coming in continually from all over the country, often from British patients of Second Sight surgeons. My long-suffering family had undertaken a 150 mile fund-raising cycle around Cuba and my ten year-old had raised over two thousand pounds with a beautifully scripted letter to JK Rowling. A few of us ran the London Marathon when we were lucky enough to get a place. However, the bottom line was that, in addition to travelling to India to find and assess new hospitals, recruiting surgeons and organising where and when they went to India, I was still the main fund-raiser. And I was still working as a locum ophthalmologist almost all the year round. In order to drive the work on faster, I needed to give Second Sight more of my time.

My partner Mark Rees is a Second Sight Trustee and the man who provides all our software needs. He is also the other family bread-winner. We needed to decide if I could cut down on my NHS work. Family discussions concluded with the decision that we could cope with my working for 6 months of the year.

I felt a tremendous freedom after this, seeing acres of time ahead of me to concentrate on expanding the work in rural north India. What I didn't anticipate was the speed at which India's economy would grow over the next few years and how this would worsen, not ameliorate, the already appalling urban-rural divide.

Chapter Sixteen

Jungle Hospital

"Life is either a great adventure or nothing"

Helen Keller

Bihar

He was waiting for us outside the railway station at Bhagalpur. You couldn't miss him. The personalised number-plate on the jeep said BISHOP -1564. A dog-collar gleaming like freshly applied gloss paint sat above a purple chest dominated by an elaborate silver cross.

He saw us, waved, and then continued to speak down his mobile phone. The driver ran to help us with our back-packs.

This was my first and last face-to-face meeting with the Bishop whose church is the dominant Protestant denomination in north India. He was then the Bishop of the Diocese of Patna and we were to visit Bamdah Christian Hospital which was located in his area. Bamdah is north India's oldest eye hospital.

Back in Britain, I had tried to recruit as a Second Sight surgeon an ophthalmologist called Kirsteen Thompson. I had heard that she was the daughter of missionary doctors, now settled in Scotland, who had grown up in Bihar. Personal circumstances prevented Kirsteen from offering to become a Second Sight volunteer but she headed me towards Bamdah Hospital which was close to where she had been born. Coincidently, a few days later I found myself working in Surrey with another ophthalmologist who had spent much of his working life in Christian charitable hospitals in India. He said:

"If ever there was a place worth trying to help it's Bamdah. It sits in the middle of one of the worst areas for blindness. But it is struggling to survive."

The third push to visit Bamdah came from another retired missionary who gave me the address and telephone number of the Bishop.

So that's how we found ourselves being picked up by the Bishop-mobile. And I heard for the first time the term "vanity plate" (personalised number-plate) from my American friend Margaret Lazarus, my travelling companion.

The Bishop took full credit for Bamdah Hospital not being already dead and buried.

"I wanted this hospital to survive" he said. "I got them an ophthalmologist. He is my brother-in-law. I persuaded him to go there."

At that stage, I was easily impressed by any claim to have persuaded an ophthalmologist to work in a remote and impoverished area. So I allotted the Bishop some brownie points. Then I got onto the subject of money. I had heard that the staff at the hospital had not been paid for a year because the hospital had to earn their wages and had not been able to do so. Couldn't his Church help to set them on their feet? The Bishop claimed that this was not his fault. He had tried to get funding from Delhi head office but without success. He suggested that I talk to them and plead Bamdah's cause. Then he put Margaret and I in a vehicle and packed us off to Bamdah.

I will just tell you here that I did go to head office in Delhi and do what the Bishop asked me to do. I fought my way past the many four--wheel drive vehicles parked outside the huge offices and had an hour's meeting with the then Head of the Health Board, across a desk that was so huge I practically needed arm extensions to shake his hand. He told me that the Health Board did not give financial assistance to any of their rural hospitals. However, if Second Sight wanted to make a donation then they would facilitate the passing on of this money to Bamdah Hospital.

I did not waste too much time chasing up north Indian church officials. But we did spend a great deal of time, energy and money on Bamdah Christian Hospital. A little part of me could not believe that a jungle eye hospital that had been carrying out thousands of cataract operations annually 50 years ago could not do so again. And Bamdah had that most precious resource, an eye surgeon apparently dedicated to working in mission hospitals for his entire life, Dr.Samuel Murmu.

Initially, however, when we tried to crank up the ailing machinery that was once north India's most famous eye hospital, there was a certain lack of co-operation from another key member of staff, a man called Maxwilliam. One winter morning at Bamdah he and I found ourselves in direct confrontation.

"Maxwilliam. Why aren't you using the new autoclave?" I asked.

There was no denying it. The tell-tale blackened stone around the stove was clear to see. Meanwhile the shiny new metal autoclave stood with the its plug face down in a sulk on the floor, its attached lead limp like a dead snake.

Silence. Maxwilliam, watery eyes set deep in a very dark, puffy face, strong firm mouth pursed under mutton-chop moustache, stood with his hands behind his back and made deliberate eye contact with me. But said nothing. I could hear, though, the whirring of his brain as he thought about the best excuse.

"Electricity supply is unreliable in these parts" he finally volunteered. Then, for more dramatic emphasis: "People are stealing it."

This was a well-known fact. Electricity supplies are non-existent or erratic in much of rural Bihar. This is partly to do with inefficient systems. But there are a host of other factors. In Bihar, one contributory factor is the 'theft' that Maxwilliam was referring to. The notoriously inefficient and corrupt state government feels no responsibility for ensuring regular electricity to the poor villages. Families with sufficient funds pay through the nose to get electricity lines to their homes. And poorer folks, the majority of the state's residents, quietly hook into them at night for their illicit share.

This is why hospitals never rely on mains electricity. An eye surgeon's instruments in an eye when the operating microscope light fails spells disaster. So Bamdah, even though in a remote jungle location, has an alternative…as Maxwilliam well knew.

" Maxwilliam, the hospital now has a reliable generator, also a reliable inverter to stabilise the unreliable voltage. There should no longer be a problem."

A few months ago I had been a total ignoramus about generators and converters and the like. So perhaps I was showing off a bit. However, I had to make a very serious point here. Instead of using the expensive new Second Sight-provided autoclave to sterilise surgical instruments, Maxwilliam had reverted back to boiling them on a gas stove. He was doing this in a side-room attached to the Operating Theatre. It was not a good arrangement. And Second Sight surgeon John Sandford Smith was coming in just a week's time to operate and to train Dr.Samuel.

"You are the most experienced Ophthalmic Assistant here, Maxwilliam. You know that the autoclave is the best way to sterilise. If you do not use it, the others will not."

Dr.Samuel lurked in the shadows, enjoying this battle of wills. However, this was the point at which he had to distance himself from Maxwilliam's intransigence, just in case any blame were allocated to him. He strolled to my side, hands in pockets.

"I have told him this. But he is not doing."

"Why not?"

His bulging dark eyes glinted with a child's glee and a huge smile cracked his face. After a precision-pause that would be the envy of a stand-up comic, he said:

"Maxwilliam doesn't like electricity."

Okay let's put this into perspective. Maxwilliam is an intelligent man of indeterminate age but roughly between 60 and 70. He is the only member of his village who is literate. He speaks several different Indian languages and has a good grasp of English.

Maxwilliam has been a dedicated employee of Bamdah Christian Hospital all his life. He can do most jobs required of trained ophthalmic assistants: giving local anaesthetic injections, sterilising the operating theatre and instruments, preparing patients for surgery.

This was obviously not just about throwing a switch. To understand Maxwilliam one has to understand the history of Bamdah Christian Hospital.

Back in 1885, Scottish missionaries came here to Bamdah and ran the hospital with superb efficiency until 1994. Like most of the staff, Maxwilliam can reel of the names of all the foreign doctors one after the other...Dr.MacPhail, Dr.Taylor, Dr.Hobson, Dr.Thompson and so forth. The staff like to recall the days of the missionary doctors: it is a way of clinging onto the glorious past when Bamdah was the most famous eye hospital in all of north India. The hospital was offering a full-scale ophthalmic service well before the days of stolen electricity in this part of the world. Indeed for years cataract operations would have been done by the light of a torch.

In 1931, a Dr.Taylor, just 23years-old and fresh out of Edinburgh Medical School, arrived in the jungle to take up a two year locum at Bamdah. He had no ophthalmic experience but was told cheerily by the departing Dr.MacPhail Jnr. that roughly *two thousand* cataract operations were performed there every year. So he set about learning from text-books. Of course it wasn't the same operation that we do now-- a micro-surgical procedure placing a plastic lens inside the eye and requiring no stitches. Nevertheless the more basic cataract operation performed by Dr.Taylor worked and with plenty of patients turning up expecting surgery, he soon became a dab hand at it. His reputation rose even further when he managed to successfully treat a temple elephant with conjunctivitis.

Black and white photos taken at that time show Dr.Taylor in the same operating theatre in which I was now standing in confrontation with Maxwilliam. The young Taylor is seen crouched over a patient on whom he is operating. I have a 21st.century picture of Second Sight surgeon John Sandford Smith in the same operating theatre operating on a child. The only differences are that he is looking down a powerful microscope and wearing the statutory hat, mask, gown and gloves of the modern eye surgeon.

Other photos from Dr.Taylor's days show hundreds of patients in the hospital grounds, some taking shelter under a majestic banyan tree, others cooking their food over small fires. Again, I have photos of our own patients doing exactly the same. The magnificent banyan tree is still standing. Sadly, the only difference in the appearance between Dr.Taylor's patients and ours is that back in the early twentieth century people appeared to have been better nourished.

After the foreign missionaries were refused permission to continue to live and work in this part of India, they handed over Bamdah to the dominant north Indian Protestant group. And the hospital rapidly deteriorated. Without the passion of the Scottish missionary doctors, without any doctors at all for some years, and without guidance and support from central office, Bamdah speedily went downhill.

When I arrived there in the year 2004 the monkeys had the upper hand, scuttling over the roofs and playing Frisbee with the broken tiles. The bell-tower had fallen down and the grass in the spacious grounds was long enough to hide a herd of elephants not just one with conjunctivitis. Ibis nested in the tall palms, their raucous calls sounding like taunts; the tall bamboos swaying in the breeze appeared to be shaking their heads in refusal.

The doctor's bungalow was occupied by Dr.Samuel, a Santali tribal doctor trained at Patna, and his paediatrician wife Sushma Minz who claimed Mau tribal ancestors. (The missionaries' converts were largely from the tribal community). Samuel and

Sushma wished to revive Bamdah as an eye hospital. But Dr.Samuel was making slow work of it. He was hardly carrying out 200 operations in a year and this in spite of having most of the latest ophthalmic equipment provided by an international Christian charity.

Maxwilliam, already worshipping daily at the altar of the departed missionary doctors, was sceptical of Dr.Samuel, cynical about his leadership of the hospital. Why should he, Maxwilliam, change the manner in which he had worked for so many years? Why shouldn't he continue to boil the instruments instead of using the new-fangled autoclave, even though, intellectually, he knew that autoclaving was the best way to sterilise.

It was time to beg.
"Maxwilliam, please. Promise me that you will use the electric autoclave. I worked so hard to get it here."

Then, this was the best bit. And perhaps I had those Scottish missionaries to be grateful to. Instead of receiving in return that totally ambiguous head-shake that people use in India for just about any response, Maxwilliam closed his eyes for a second and nodded. A definitive affirmative. Yeess!

I probably should not have worried so much about Maxwilliam's intransigence because the person who was to take Bamdah in hand over the next two years was more than capable of dealing with anything thrown his way.

I first met 72 year-old John Sandford Smith in a pub in London's Islington area. He was very clear about how he would prefer to contribute to Second Sight. Leaning his tall but slight frame against the bar, he downed his pint with vigour and in his gentle voice stated firmly that, if possible, he would like to train doctors whom I felt might stay working in rural India. He would prefer this to curing hundreds of blind people himself.

Frankly, I was thrilled that such an experienced global ophthalmologist was considering getting involved in Second Sight. John had lived and worked on three continents and had written two excellent books on eye diseases and eye surgery in hot climates. He had trained diverse groups of people to become ophthalmic surgeons from Burmese nuns to doctors in the Yemen. In his books, John pays respect to global initiatives like Vision 2020 A Right to Sight. But warns that they are wasted if they cannot be translated into reality where they are most needed: amongst the poorest communities in the world. He was just the kind of person I wanted involved in Second Sight.

When it came to training, John and I thought along the same lines. We both believed that training surgeons on-site, in the rural environment in which you wanted them to continue to work, was far more effective than sending them off on courses at well-equipped hospitals in cities; too often they were seduced by the prospects in city private practice and never returned to the countryside. John had seen many examples of this in his years working in developing countries. I knew that none of the Indian trainees on the surgical course I had attended in south India had ended up working in rural areas, even those originally from the countryside. We agreed that Training had to be properly planned so that there was the greatest chance possible of the trainee-surgeon using his or her skills where they were most needed.

A few months before meeting John I had had a similar conversation, with a different outcome, with a man in India. He was attached to one of the largest eye training institutes in the south of the country, although not an ophthalmologist himself. Send the northern doctors to us, he had said, we can train them properly. We can train them properly, too, I had asserted. But at their own hospitals. That is not what most people did, he argued. Most foreign NGOs arrange training at places like his institute because of its reputation and high standards. But what was the point if they ended up in private practice and in cities, I asked. He got a little defensive. That was not the case, he insisted. But what had he got against the idea of training on-site, I persisted. It cannot be done properly, he said. This was stale-mate. There is usually a sub-text in conversations with educated middle-class Indians that the rural north-east is an uncivilized place and trainers cannot be expected to go there.

With John Sandford Smith it was an entirely different story.

I described Bamdah. I explained about the lack of a flush toilet and erratic electricity supply in the doctor's bungalow. I told him about the rundown buildings and mildewed walls in many of the hospital buildings. I told him that the paramedic staff were totally dedicated but had had little formal training. And that teaching Dr.Samuel was going to be hard work.

"But is he willing to learn?" asked John.

"Yes."

"And do you think he is going to stay working at Bamdah?"

"Yes. In fact, his wife Sushma told me that he had married her on condition that she agreed that they would both work at mission hospitals all their lives."

John ended up making five month-long visits over two years. Samuel made slow progress but by the end he was not just a competent eye surgeon but able to deal with most ophthalmic conditions with considerable more knowledge and understanding than previously. Dr.Samuel is still working in rural Bihar and I have every confidence that he will stay there. With only 20% of India's ophthalmologists working in the rural areas, every competent eye surgeon in the countryside is a precious resource. In rural Bihar more than anywhere else.

Bamdah was also the unlikely setting of one truly memorable case. It is a tale that will go down in the annals of Second Sight.

A youngish man arrived in the Out-patients Department. He had had cataract surgery about ten years ago but as a result of poor surgical technique the cornea (the normally transparent surface of the eye) had been damaged. It was now so hazy the man could not see through this eye at all. He was blind once again.

Through the clinical examination, John deduced that the retina at the back of this 'blind' eye was still functional. Meanwhile, the patient's other eye had a perfectly healthy cornea but the eye had been non-seeing for years from an irreversible cause.

So the man had a healthy cornea in the eye that was irreversibly blind and a healthy retina in the eye with the ruined cornea. He was ideal for an autologous corneal transplant: swapping the corneas around would give him sight in one eye. What's more there was no risk of rejection as the tissue was his own!

The only specialist instrument that was required that Bamdah certainly did not have was a trephine (for removing the corneas). But John is never one to be caught out in remote locations; he carries certain instruments with him. He performed the autologous graft with no problems, and to the delight and awe of the hospital paramedical staff who, fleetingly, felt what it was like to be part of cutting-edge ophthalmology.

I was at Bamdah a few weeks later with my friend Lin Brown, a non-medical volunteer for Second Sight. Something was very different as we approached the village. All the stalls were boarded up, there were no people about. Overlooking the hospital compound was a new police watch-tower, close enough for us to see the police-wallahs' guns pointed in our direction.

When we reached the hospital Dr.Samuel informed us that a local resident alleged to be a 'police informer' had been shot dead by Naxalites-- Maoist/communist activists who for years have been in confrontation with the police. There was now curfew from dusk to dawn. In spite of this, the hospital building was bustling with post-operative patients on whom Dr.John and Samuel had operated. Including the man who had had the successful corneal transplant. When I examined him I found he had good vision and the graft looked healthy. He was a happy man.

After the clinic was over, I climbed up to the flat roof of the doctors' bungalow with my binoculars. The bird life in Bamdah is superb. I wanted to watch the Ibis in their tree-top nests who had appeared so haughty on my first visit and also the common hornbills who had made a spreading fruit tree their favourite haunt.

I heard the padding of soft shoes and Dr.Samuel's father-in-law emerged from the stairs and greeted me. Then he placed his hands on my shoulders and began to gently swivel me around.

"Dr.Lucy," he said, still smiling. "You can look that way, and that way and that way. But please don't look in the direction of the tower. Otherwise the police-wallahs will shoot you."

Itching to train the binoculars on the tower to get a closer look at the police officers, I nevertheless obeyed orders.

"So was it like this when Dr. John was here?" I asked

"Yes. The curfew began the day he arrived. The police-wallahs were here throughout Dr.John's stay."

I then vaguely remembered John's passing reference in his report to the presence of the police at Bamdah, a reference buried in more important and helpful facts about the state of Samuel's surgical skills, the individual needs of the paramedics, the financial state of the hospital, and of course his report on the corneal transplant. I also recalled two other Second Sight surgeons reporting back to me about their trip to Raxaul; they happily told me about the number of patients cured and the excellence of the paramedic staff and towards the end of the conversation just mentioned that their train had been delayed half a day. I remembered surgeon Andy Richards, like John, a septuagenarian, being whisked across the Indo-Nepalese border on the back of a motorbike when trains and buses were not working during a strike, and calling me, not to complain but to reassure me that he could start operating on time.

I told all this to Lin that night, as we stood under a Bamdah sky studded with brilliant stars but no moon. I said that I had never anticipated that we would get so deeply and personally involved with communities in rural India and that this involvement would take us to the most neglected and volatile areas. I had simply followed my nose to find the forgotten blind and had found an entirely forgotten India. While it was no real surprise to me that I was slipping deeper and deeper into this world, I was still rather amazed that everyone connected with Second Sight so gamely followed in my path. They seemed to just get on with whatever task they had come to do.

Lin had worked in television for most of her life. Indeed, it was she who had organized that seminal trip to Afghanistan when I had had my Damascene experience and had decided to retrain as a doctor. Her greatest skill, as far as I am concerned, is an almost instinctive understanding of how people tick, whether it is an old woman in a village refusing to get on the hospital bus waiting to take her for surgery or a bureaucrat being economical with the truth. I asked Lin why she thought people continued to volunteer for Second Sight.

"Everyone wants to be a fixer," she said. "Whether it is fixing eyes or fixing water-pumps."

Having been personally responsible for installing Bamdah Hospital's new water-pump Lin was obviously speaking from experience.

As for the Bishop of Bamdah? Well, there was one other rare sighting. He popped in to meet John Sandford Smith and his loyal wife Sheila towards the end of their first month there. And stayed just long enough to chide them for such a brief stay. The former missionary-doctors used to stay and work at Bamdah for all their lives, he said, not just for four weeks. Then off he went in the jeep with the vanity plate.

I never caught sight of the Bishop ever again. But I retain a kind of twitcher's fascination with him. I hear that he became the Chairman of the Synodical Board of Health Services for his entire organisation. And, on latest surfing of their website I see that he is Deputy Moderator (I think that's No.2 in the hierarchy).

I do wonder if he has changed the vanity plate.

Chapter Seventeen

A Jewel in Bihar

If you drive south-west from Bamdah, you can cross into neighbouring Jharkhand state and pick up the main highway that goes back into Bihar. It is not a journey that many do. And it has its hallucinatory moments. You can be lulled into total relaxation driving through beautiful and varied countryside: gigantic smooth-surfaced boulders bordering bubbling brooks one hour, large expanses of paddy fields the next. You can stop at small tea-stalls and drink your chai watching skinny children cavort their way past you, arms slung around each other and cheeky laughs thrown over their shoulders. You can distinguish different tribal groups from the colourful patterns drawn on the outside walls of their mud-huts. It can feel idyllic.

Then you can turn a corner and a totally bleak image whacks you in the face and time seems to stop as you absorb it. Like your first sight of the 'koilawallahs', the coal-men of Jharkhand. From a distance they look like a line of giant black ants moving in single file along the black tarmac. There is no colour to be seen. As you draw closer you see that they are emaciated, very dark men, arms spread to full expansion across bags of coal that are piled across their cycles, unstable burdens that could fall at any moment without the men's' intent concentration. Man and machine strain to move the burdens. The procession moves at snail's pace, sometimes appearing not to move at all. It is like looking at a black and white photograph of a ghastly procession of crucified figures.

The coal is scavenged or given in return for bribes to security guards at open mines dug by private contractors or state-owned enterprises. The koilawallahs too exhausted to push the bikes over the brow of the hills pay a few rupees to other men waiting at each steep incline.

Hallucinatory moments in Bihar can also come in the way of pleasant surprises. Another corner turned in another road and you can fall into a world so at odds with its surroundings that it is surreal. This was my experience when I first visited Gems at Sikaria near Dehri-on-Sone.

I was taken there, once again, by Jone Wills the indefatigable CEO of the Jiwan Jyoti Christian Hospital at Roberstganj. He knew what was required of a hospital to become a Second Sight partner. He was certain that Gems had what it takes. But he knew that no big decision was ever taken at Gems except by the man in charge, Augustine Jebakumar. I will take you to Gems said Jone and introduce you to "Brother Augustine" he said.

The last section of the journey took us through dusty village after dusty village populated by men and women who looked thoroughly worn out. The dilapidated huts did not improve but the road suddenly did.

"Do you know who Lalu is, Lucy?" asked Jone Wills.

"Yes, the notorious Chief Minister of Bihar" I replied.

This was before the historic election that removed Lalu Prasad from the top job after fifteen years in power.

Jone laughed.

"Well, Augustine wanted to have a tarmacked road leading to Gems. Of course, getting permission is difficult here. So he decided to invite the Chief Minister himself to visit Gems. They even built a heliport for his private helicopter. Lalu stepped out of the helicopter, looked around him and said, oh I had no idea that we had such wonderful institutions in Bihar! Permission for the road was given."

In the next moment the wonderful place was there to see for myself. But what impressed me was the fact that the very- Hindu Chief Minister Lalu Prasad had given his blessing to the place. You see, GEMS stands for Gospel Echoing Missionary Society. And it is the most In- Your- Face Evangelical Christian establishment I had ever come across in rural north India, sitting right in the heart of the so-called Hindu Cow Belt. What's more, it is run by South Indian Christians who have imported many of their permanent management staff from the south.

I stepped from the jeep and my eyes were immediately drawn to a large globe atop a handsome church, a world held up by a pair of brown hands. From the church came singing and the sound of an electric piano. Outside there was laughter and giggling as hundreds of bonny school-children, many of them on crutches and in adapted cycles, propelled themselves past us and shouted at me "Blessed be in Christ, Auntie". A few teachers ushered them on their way but did not attempt to curb their enthusiasm.

The lively atmosphere everywhere was created by the mass of children who dominated most of the Gems campus. Many of these were children who had first arrived at Gems on their hands and knees, crippled by polio. They were given reconstructive surgery and physiotherapy, and stay in a residential home until their secondary schooling (also provided on the campus) is complete.

"Brother Augustine" turned out to be a hirsute, bear of a man with a huge smile and a huge laugh. He had come to that corner of Bihar 30 years ago he said, because he wanted to live and work amongst the poorest people. He had been an engineer in south India but felt a direct calling from God. From small beginnings Gems has grown into a massive place: primary and secondary schools, colleges, training centres and an IT block.

As we chatted with Augustine in his home, a relative brought in a small baby.

"This is our latest addition to the family" he told us. "She was dumped on a railway track. A dog picked her up by the arm and she started to cry. Some villagers heard her and rescued her from the dog. They brought her here because they knew we would take her in. The arm had to be amputated."

The little one-armed girl let out a loud wail as if to demonstrate the crying power that had saved her life. A few years later when I visited Gems again, I got a cameo-glimpse of her ...a confident toddler, shoving away an older sibling with her one arm as they battled over a toy.

"We used to have an experienced ophthalmic assistant," said Augustine. "But she left after a year."

"And why do you think that was?" I asked.

He paused.

"I think that perhaps our level of Christianity was a bit too scary for her" he said. And roared with laughter.

"Augustine, believe me, it *is* scary," I replied. He laughed even harder.

Regardless of the overpoweringly evangelical Christian atmosphere at Gems, I decided to send a rota of volunteer eye surgeons. And, as it turned out, the person who loved it more than anyone else was Second Sight surgeon Andy Richards, a non-believer when it comes to formal religions. He once made two visits in the space of three months and cured nearly 500 blind patients.

The time had come, however, to recruit more volunteer doctors from within India. The country with the worst cataract blindness problem also contained some of the world's best cataract surgeons. Time was speeding by. And we needed them.

Chapter Eighteen

The north south divide

By 2007 most Second Sight surgeons were still from Britain. The regular volunteers came from Newcastle, London, Southampton and Burnley, from Wales and from Northern Ireland. None of them batted an eyelid about going to rural Bihar. When I tried to recruit south Indian surgeons, however, they reeled back in horror. It's okay people going from England to Bihar, but "for us Indians" Bihar is…and their words would trail off ominously. Some did not want to go anywhere north Or rural. Except for Rajasthan because that was pretty.

Much of the prejudice against places like Bihar is fed by stereotypical reporting in the mainstream Indian Press. I decided that is was time for some counter-propaganda. I would make a video. For a year, my video-camera became a constant appendage and I recorded extensive material from every hospital to which we had ever sent a Second Sight surgeon and from every village I had visited. I took close-ups of equipment and videoed operating theatres and told the stories of staff and patients. I had a lot of fun editing my material and satisfied my creative urges by adding music and effects.

We chose Bangalore in the state of Karnataka as the first southern city to hit with our Second Sight Road Show. This was possibly a little foolish as Bangalore is an expensive place and I was paying for it all out of my own pocket. I was tempted, however, by the fact that the affluent IT city was knee-deep in ophthalmologists. I was told this by Raghu Ram, a Second Sight surgeon from Cardiff, who also had contacts at the Bangalore Club.

When the Secretary of the Karnataka State Ophthalmologists Society, Santhan Gopal, turned out to be the first Consultant under whom I had worked in England, I felt a Bangalore event was meant to be.

"Are you the same Lucy who used to ride her cycle from Luton station every day?" he asked on the phone when I called to get the list of ophthalmologists.

Perhaps on the strength of my cycling history I was given the entire list of Bangalore ophthalmologists and offered an office from which to work. Santhan, however, said he doubted we would get a single recruit. There is big money in India now, he said, and everyone in Bangalore is too busy trying to get some of it. Private practice was very lucrative in the IT city, he told me rather smugly. If they're earning so much they can afford to give up one lousy week of their time, I retorted.

My French friend, Bene Pareil (met whilst trekking in the Himalayas) offered to help organise the event. And I arranged for Dr.Helen Rao to come from Bihar. She was my trump card: a southerner who had devoted her entire working life to practising ophthalmology in rural Bihar.

All was going well and then two days before the event, a charming woman at the Bangalore Club broke the news to us that club rules forbad videos being shown at gatherings. Damn, I said. De rien, said Bene, I will make copies and we will send them to the ophthalmologists. This is India, Lucy, you can do these things quick and fast. And she did. She made 100 copies and delivered them by hand!

About 50 ophthalmologists turned up. They were greeted by Bene, ushered over to me, and then went off to speak to Dr.Helen. Raghu was also there to prove that Second Sight surgeons who boldly go where others fear to tread actually do return in one piece.

The assembled ophthalmologists were, frankly, amazed. I don't know what they were expecting but it certainly wasn't three ophthalmologists and a beautiful French-woman all beside themselves with enthusiasm for curing blind patients in India's most unpopular state. We encouraged them to join us.

I had a lot of nice emails and phone-calls afterwards telling me how inspired people had felt by the event. There was not a rush of volunteers. However, one excellent doctor, Veeresh Akki, was operating at Helen's unit within six months of the Bangalore event and that started the ball rolling. I shall never erase his email to me after he returned to Bangalore.

"Thank you for sending me to Bihar. This was the best personal and professional experience of my life."

We took the Second Sight Road Show deeper south, to the state of Kerala. There I found the man who had run the Indian surgical training course I had taken part in all those years ago and during which the seed of Second Sight had been planted. Dr.Arup Chakrabarti and his ophthalmologist-wife Meena placed a timely insert in the Kerala Ophthalmologists' Journal and, as a result, some excellent eye surgeons came on board the Second Sight team.

Satisfying also was the fact that Kerala journalists played a part in our recruitment drive. This was due to a family link. My late father's ancestral home is in Kerala and the Malayalam Manorama newspaper was founded by my great great uncle. A phone-call to the 92year-old Editor, also a distant relative, resulted in a nice article commending the descendant of the "famous Kandathil family" (me!) for thinking about the blind in India, and exhorting Kerala's eye surgeons to play their part. My old Dad would have been proud.

When the busy operating season began in October 2008, Second Sight surgeons from India outnumbered those from the UK. This was a huge achievement. We were on a roll.

Chapter Nineteen

Slaughtering the ox

In early 2009 we all lost our sense of humour.

We were in the midst of our most successful year yet. We were aiming to have cured our 30,000th blind patient by the autumn. We had defied the cynics who said that India's ophthalmologists were driven purely by the pursuit of money and Indian surgeons now outnumbered those from the UK. Some had already done stints at our partner hospitals, leaving behind evidence of their great skill and leaving with a new view of areas of their country that they would never have otherwise visited.

I had made an important breakthrough with funders, too. More donors had absorbed the important fact that India's blindness problem would never be solved if the worst areas were continually ignored. And we were one of only a few organisations actually working in these areas.

Central to our progress in Bihar was Dr.Helen Rao's unit at The Duncan Hospital at Raxaul. Her meticulous outreach programme went deep into the forests and remote villages, treating minor ailments and prescribing glasses and bringing in the cataract blind for surgery. Visiting surgeons from India's big south Indian metropolises like Bangalore, some of whom had not seen hyper-mature cataracts for years, were amazed that every single patient on whom they operated was blind. They soon forgot their reservations about travelling to notorious Bihar state and worked hard to cure as many people as they could during their short stays. They were humbled by the fact that Dr.Helen, herself from the south of India, had dedicated her life to Bihar's poor. Second Sight surgeons enjoyed working at Raxaul so much I had too many applying to go there and had to work hard to persuade them that our other partner hospitals were also excellent places.

Then the central Delhi office of the large Christian group that ran The Duncan Hospital dropped their bombshell. There was an official retirement age of 58. In the year 2009 Helen reached this age. She would have to retire and leave by May 31.

Surely some mistake we thought. We knew that there were plenty of people in the organisation who had been allowed to stay on well after this age.

Looking at the wider picture we were even more certain that this was all one big misunderstanding on the part of the management in central office in New Delhi. Their hospitals and eye departments in particular, were desperate to attract and retain ophthalmologists. We had formed partnerships with two departments, at Robertsganj and at Raxaul, but I had visited and been asked to help four others within the same group. With so many eye departments struggling, why on earth would they want to tamper with one that was growing more successful each year? In fact, for over 20 years Dr.Helen's unit had been providing the *only* reliable eye service in their entire group of hospitals! And this in a huge swathe of north-western Bihar in which there was absolutely no other eye hospital for the poor.

Perhaps central management in Delhi were not aware of this. Or else we were not aware of some grand plan that might even improve on what already existed.

I met the organisation's Managing Director in Delhi, along with Rebecca Peltenburg and Francisca Van Holthoon from two charitable trusts who support us.

So, was there an ophthalmologist ready to take over from Dr.Helen? we asked.

No there was not.

Did he realise that if Dr.Helen went that was effectively shutting down one of their most successful eye departments?

Well, the "local management" had some "alternative arrangements" he said.

Could we know what these were? We had after all been heavily involved with the hospital for over six years.

No, he did not have the details.

Wouldn't it make more sense to allow Dr.Helen to stay on and for us all to work together to find a suitable replacement? This way the patients would not be left in the lurch?

It was not his decision. He would have to talk to the local hospital management.

We appeared to be getting nowhere. Then I remembered that I shared something with this man that the others did not. He might be the Managing Director of the organisation, but he was also, like me, a doctor.

"Look, can we forget for one moment about the different organisations that we represent," I said. "I want to appeal to you, one doctor to another. Imagine if you had set up a thriving department and, just as it was at its most successful, they wanted to shut it down. Don't you think you would fight it? Don't you think that you would be thinking first and foremost of your patients?"

There was a flicker in his eyes. As if I had reminded him of a past life that he was struggling to recall. The flicker signalled that he was uncomfortable. But there was no empathy in it.

A few weeks later we received an email stating that the decision that Dr.Helen should retire by May 31 stood, and that the "eye services at Duncan will be without leadership" after that!

Of course it was all internal politics. But the huge consequences for the people of north-western Bihar appalled us. Our pleas and protestations had no affect.

"Health and education today, hope for tomorrow."

This is the Vision statement on their website. Yet with one destructive political decision, they removed the hope of thousands of blind people.

We appealed to the German-based international Christian charity that had supplied all the ophthalmic equipment to Helen's department over many years. Surely they did not want their equipment to lie unused and for blind patients to be turned away? They were not ready to interfere.

It is no wonder that Second Sight surgeon John Sandford Smith, himself a devout Christian, wrote angrily to the Managing Director of the hospital group:

"There is a warning in the New Testament "not to muzzle the ox when it is treading out the grain", but it seems that you don't want to just muzzle the ox but to slaughter and bury it."

Not being a devout Christian myself, my own violent thoughts were not related to oxen.

Chapter Twenty

Future will happen

Rajasthan, India

"You are wanting to see saint?" asked Rajmal Jain.
"What kind of saint?" I asked nervously.
"He is telling future."
"Mmm. Don't really want to know my future."
"I am thinking same. Future will happen."

Worrying about the future of Second Sight was actually what had brought me back to Rajasthan. It wasn't that I expected to get any specific advice from Rajmal. I just needed to bask in the soothing environment of the Shree Bhairav Eye Hospital and to be with my old friends; to sit quietly with Rajmal on either side of the desk at which the first major Second Sight decision had been taken and to remind myself, just by being there, of how much had been achieved since that initial meeting.

I had briefly ranted about the Raxaul affair, feeling free to complain bitterly about the politics of large organisations in the presence of a man who had had thirty years of experience in dealing with this and who had kept his integrity throughout. Rajmal had responded with characteristic ellipsis.

"Meetings, meetings, meetings.Always they are deciding in meetings. Poor patient cannot come to meetings."

Then he had set about trying to bolster my flagging morale.

In the early days of the Bhairav Eye Hospital, he told me, his one and only eye surgeon came to him one day and demanded a ludicrously high pay increase. Rajmal said no. The doctor packed his bags and drove out of the hospital grounds.

"I am watching his car turn left side out of Bhairav Hospital gates. I am worried, thinking, now hospital has no eye surgeon. Very bad. Then, coming from right side is one more car. It is surgeon who worked at Bhairav in past. He is coming to offer his services again."

"Lucky" I commented.
"Yes, lucky" agreed Rajmal.

Then he continued:

"One other time, government is asking Rajmal to pay crores (millions) of rupees in fines. They are saying that planning permission was not given for hospital extension. Hospital could not afford such a fine. So I am calling public meeting. Many many people are here in hospital lobby. I tell Government officials: three things you can do. Bring bull-dozers and destroy hospital. Take over hospital as government enterprise. Or leave Bhairav Hospital alone to continue our good work. After this we had no problem."

"That's a good story" I said, feeling genuinely cheered by this example of successful brinkmanship.

Rajmal had responded with a satisfied smile and then had brought up the subject of the Saint. My initial disinterest in seeing the Holy Man was not allowed to rest.

"Saint is knowing past as well as future," he said.

"Really? Well that could be interesting," I conceded.

So Rajmal and I agreed to meet this particular Holy Man. We decided we should ask for a shared consultation with him so that we could compare notes afterwards in a thoroughly objective way.

Three days later, I was sitting in front of a bonny young man with a shock of thick black hair who rocked himself back and forth at a frantic pace and spoke so fast it made you dizzy to listen. He wore a spotless white robe and the vermilion 'tilak' on his forehead worn by all holy men. He was carrying out Rajmal's consultation and I was just an observer at this stage which gave me time to adjust to sitting cross-legged in my borrowed outfit.

Rajmal's female relatives had whisked me off to the bedrooms and, in twenty seconds flat, had stripped me of my black outer clothing. I was handed a yellow shalwar kameez outfit and many bangled hands proffered help with dressing. Then one of the older women interrupted crossly and pointed, accusingly, at my Marks and Spencer crop top and knickers.

"Off. Off. You cannot wear black."

"Oh come now…the saint won't even know I am wearing black underwear" I said in light-hearted vein.

A few of the younger women snickered.

"Do not make fun of saint" chided the older woman.

Off with the knickers. Off with the crop top. Air squeezed out of me by an extremely tight-fitting bodice, yellow outfit pulled down to cover all and a dupatta wound around my head.

"I am *so* uncomfortable" I moaned.

"Don't worry. Now you can see saint" said the old crone and smiled, quite sweetly.

Your clothes are nicer, I heard in a muffled tone through my head-scarf. A couple of gigglers beat a hasty retreat before they could be identified.

And now here we were in the saint's presence, and he was really a very cheerful soul. He started the consultation by smacking a small desk-bell with the palm of his hand and glancing briefly at an alarm clock next to it.

Ping. Then the torrent of words began and I was lost. Rajmal, on the other hand was practically swooning with admiration merely five minutes in. It seems the saint was getting it all right: yes Rajmal had had major abdominal surgery, yes he had given up mangoes when Number 2 brother survived his bypass surgery and apples when Number 3 brother had survived something else and yes, it was certainly correct that Rajmal had started life as a businessman but was now doing "social work."

Then Rajmal, in spite of having scoffed about wishing to know the future, asked about the eye hospital: who would be his successor, who would take over from him?

The saint smiled reassuringly and mentioned as a likely candidate for this role Rajmal's younger brother, already a committed humanitarian running a deaf and dumb school. Ecstasy on Rajmal's face.

Ping. His time was over.

He moved across and made space for me in front of the saint's little table. The saint smiled and asked Rajmal a question.

"Saint is asking how far is London" Rajmal enquired.

"Three thousand miles?"

A Hindi exchange took place.

"Saint is saying this is outside his limit. But he will try."

And then, ping, off we went. Back and forth he rocked, smiling all the while, words (in English? In Hindi?) pouring out of his mouth and Rajmal, once more, shaking his head in disbelief and smiling happily. Just when I thought it was all baloney, there it was "thwack thwack", the saint thumped both his forearms and...stopped.

"Oh My God" intoned Rajmal.

What? What did he say?

"Saint is saying, Lucy is always having good health. Then in one year she is having two accidents."

Oh my God. My broken arms. I had fractured both wrists within a year whilst playing football. Now that was impressive.

Like Rajmal, previously scornful about clairvoyant predictions, I found myself wanting to ask about the future of Second Sight. Having suddenly and mysteriously become a believer in fortune-tellers, I wanted to ask if we would be able to pick ourselves up after the biggest disappointment in our existence?

But it was not to be.

Ping. My time was up.

Ah, well. Future will happen.

PART FOUR

Back on course

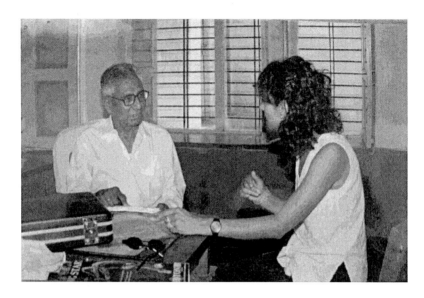

The author with Rajmal Jain in Rajasthan.

Shree Bhairav Eye Hospital driver Champalal.

Rajasthani magicians.

The author with Dennis Kendall(L) and Thakur Sahib (R) in the Himalayas.

Dr. Helen's Eye, Raxaul, Bihar.

Dr. Helen(R) and patient Lalpari Devi (L).

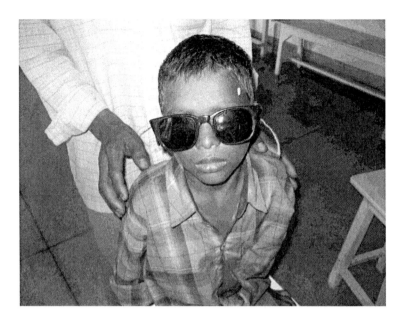

Paediatric Patient, Bamdah Hospital.

Shaving in the jungle. Dr. John Sandford Smith at Bamdah Hospital.

Fund raising cycle in Cuba. Lucy and son Calum after fifty miles.

Football at Mastichak. The game that started it all.

Mritunjay Tiwari with the children of the diara.

The TN team. Dr. Shiva front row second right.

The author, Dr. Shiva and Subala and Ranjit.

A rare moment of leisure. Second Sight surgeon Andy Richards.

Happiness in Bihar.

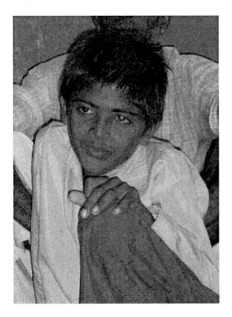

10 year-old Suresh who took the cover photograph. Blind until his cataract operation.

Mastichak footballers at hospital for English and IT classes.

L to R : Auditor Himanshu Ashar, Ophthalmic trainee Sushma Kumari,
Farmer Awadh Rai, Lucy Mathen, Coach Madhu Singh, Surgeon Ajeet Kumari Dwivedi,
Mritunjay Tiwari. Front row L to R : Footballer Parveen, Ramesh Chandra Shukla,
Optometrist Roisin Cox and Imam Irshad Ahmed

CHAPTER Twenty-one

Feng shui future

Mastichak, Bihar

The bird of prey swooping over the field caught our attention. We stopped in our tracks, our host Mritunjay Tiwari in the front, Francisca and I behind him, with a long trail of village children who had been following us all the way.

"Pigeon," said Mritunjay.

"Pigeon!?" said Francisca.

"Baaj" said a boy, pointing to the bird.

"Oh, it's an eagle" said Mritunjay.

Then, laughing: "Okay, I'm a city boy."

He might not know his birds, but 39year-old Kolkata marketing-man Mritunjay Tiwari has an extraordinary grasp of how to run a successful rural eye hospital and an enthusiasm that matches this.

You cannot help but smile when you see Mritunjay in action. He has lithe quick movements, never sitting still for long; he makes big sweeping gestures to emphasise points when talking to a group; he has an endearingly confiding manner of slipping an arm around the shoulders of an individual member of staff, and almost whispering instructions as if only that one person is capable of the job to be done.

He talks fast, moves fast, acts fast and implements fast. His full-throttle approach pays dividends: the Akhand Jyoti Eye Hospital may be located in a small remote village but the professionalism and high standards of its staff rival that of any prestigious teaching hospital in India.

In addition, the AJEH must surely deserve the Second Sight prize for aesthetics. It's a colour-fest from the moment you step past the gates.

It begins with meeting the Chairman of the Yogrishi Shriram Sharma Acharya Charitable Trust, the secular, non-profitable and non-political NGO that runs the hospital. Pandit Ramesh Chandra Shukla is a gentle giant dressed in saffron with a pure white Gandalf-beard down to his waist and an elaborate tilak on his forehead in the shape of a trident, the weapon of the Hindu God Lord Shiva. He is 90years-old and suffers from swollen ankles, poor soul, but is often at the hospital keeping an eye on things. And smiling with pride at Mritunjay who is so obviously running the place with great style and determination.

Outside the main entrance, patients are given different coloured tags to wear around their necks depending on whether they are for surgery or for out-patients. The colour-coding for the staff was explained to me by Mritunjay.

"When we started we used to use the universal hospital colour of green for operating theatre staff. While talking to patients, although not said explicitly we came to understand that patients were generally wary of surgery, and green symbolised that. So we decided to use several colours in the operating theatre so that a mental reassurance came to the patients that we are *different* from others. Furthermore use of several colours makes the setup look more cheerful and a person entering the Operating Theatre for the first time would gaze at different colours present inside and would divert his mind away from the apprehensions regarding surgery."

"Alright, Mr.Marketing Man," I interjected. "But tell me how the surgeons ended up with lovely pink gowns."

"Okay, okay," he continued at pace. "As for the actual choice of colour, we consulted our chairman. He suggested some colours based on the ancient Hindu system of Vaastu. The colours yellow and orange symbolizing physical and spiritual strength, pink symbolizing strong relationships and caring attitude, and blue symbolizing the sky and tranquility."

"The boys assisting the surgeons chose the colour for the surgeons. And the surgeons chose the colour for them. In this way the doctors ended up with bright pink, the scrub-nurses bright orange and the other ophthalmic assistants a soothing blue."

The final colour in this scheme is beige, the colour of the surgical masks and also the clothing of visitors wishing to observe proceedings in the operating theatre. All the hospital's washing is hung out to dry on the roof of the main building. This means that on most days there is a kaleidoscope of gorgeous colours waving in the breeze, bright and cheerful adverts for a thriving hospital.

On the AJEH website Mritunjay has written:

"Our economy is growing and healthcare is a sunrise industry with corporates and multinationals joining the fray every day. The fight is for the pockets of the 40per cent of Indians in cities and towns. What about the other 60per cent with lesser resources?"

Mritunjay is well able to talk about these two very different Indias. Although his ancestral village is near Mastichak, the location of the hospital, his family are now comfortably settled in Kolkata. He could easily have ended up using his skills in the "sunrise" industry of private healthcare that is, truly, making some very rich. He could have been a fat cat in Calcutta. Instead he moves around the Akhand Jyoti Hospital with the boundless energy of a kitten and refuses to be put down by set-backs. And he has had his fair share of these.

He showed me the Memorandum of Understanding signed in the year 2006, with an international charity which promised two years of financial support. Three months after the hospital opened, they changed their minds and pulled out of the agreement. They did not give a reason, but in their letter terminating the contract, expressed confidence that the AJEH would be able to keep going. And also took credit for helping to build the hospital's "capacity and credibility" in the area.

Off the record, the then Mumbai-head of this NGO advised Mritunjay to close down and reapply in 18months when they might have more funds! Wow, that would have done wonders for our "credibility" in the villages around Mastichak, remarked Mritunjay when relating this story.

The AJEH didn't shut up shop. Everyone simply pulled together. And Mritunjay and the Trust that runs the hospital mobilised a formidable host of supporters and volunteers to keep the hospital work going. The patients were never let down. In 2008, the AJEH eye surgeons carried out 13,000 operations.

Elated by their success in spite of the broken financial promise, Mritunjay and hospital external auditor Himanshu Ashar took themselves off to a management course at a famous Eye Institute in south India. Perhaps they could still learn something to make the AJEH even more successful, they had thought. The course was on "The Model Rural Eye Hospital".

By the end of the lectures, both Mritunjay and Himanshu were amazed. Their own AJEH appeared to meet none of the criteria for a successful rural eye hospital. Himanshu, an urbane and knowledgeable city auditor, felt he could not allow the course attendees, who came from all over the world, to go away thinking that there was only one model for a rural hospital that could possibly work. So he asked the course leader to write a few things up on the board.

How could a hospital be both sustainable and eradicate cataract blindness asked Himanshu, given the following restraints: number one, no electricity supply within 15 kilometres.

The course leader wrote this on the board.

Number two, continued Himanshu, very limited skills and low education of available manpower for the lower and mid level staff.

At this point the course lecturer commented that core members of a hospital's human resources team should really have MBAs.

Himanshu ploughed on. Number three: the average income per family of the majority of patients using the hospital was less than 500 rupees per month and the average family size 7-8 members.

The lecturer co-operatively wrote this on the board, in full knowledge that the 500 rupees income per month was less than the charge for a cataract operation at his own "model rural hospital."

The fifth point Himanshu asked him to write up on the board was: no towns nearby from which to get paying patients or to be attractive to ophthalmologists. Then the shrewd auditor played his trump card. He asked the course leader to write these precise words on the board: withdrawal of promised funds by the main financial backer, an international NGO, after just three months.

Turning from the board, the course leader said that he did not think such a hospital could ever survive.

"Well it has," announced Himanshu. "We are in rural Bihar. And we have carried out over 30,000 operations since 2005."

The room silently applauded.

After telling me this tale, Mritunjay commented that perhaps if they had not had their funds withdrawn so dramatically by the international charity, they would not have grown to be so confident about questioning the practises and advice of other well-established organisations. I told him that, in the same way, if I had not received that letter from DFID when I had first started Second Sight, stating that curing the blind was not "empowering" the poor, I might not have become so determined to prove them wrong.

The AJEH had not existed when we first started working in north India. But it was a happy discovery in the tenth year of our existence. We had 'found' them thanks to some lateral thinking on the part of a friend, Ruban Inba, who lives in Delhi. I had explained to Ruban that although I had travelled extensively around Bihar and knew most of the hospitals engaged in eye-care,

I had a strong suspicion that I might be missing a hospital in the mould of Rajmal Jain's Shree Bhairav Eye Hospital in Rajasthan: a truly model rural eye hospital that was a central part of the local community.

Ruban had asked the representative from a company which manufactured intra-ocular lenses if he delivered a substantial amount of equipment to any rural hospital in Bihar. He had expected the answer to be no. But the man had immediately mentioned the AJEH. A few months later we were there.

I had grown so used to hearing people from Bihar (especially those who had relocated) talking about the state in disparaging terms, that I was astounded to hear Mritunjay's obvious pride in the place. And the hospital staff, who had never heard the views of an outsider, were equally astounded to hear of our genuine affection for their state.

"We are Biharis and we want to sort out the problems that poverty brings to our state," said Mritunjay. "But you come all the way from Britain and you seem to care as much about this as all of us here. You and your ophthalmologists have been working to help the blind in rural Bihar even before the AJEH. This makes me want to work harder. If you had not come along we would have still continued this work. But we are currently running at about 50kilometres an hour. Working with you we can run at twice that speed."

"Brilliant!" I replied. "Let's do it. Let's make Bihar lead the way in north India. That will surprise everyone."

"Definitely we can do that," replied Mritunjay.

If either of us felt nervous about taking on this awesome challenge we did not show it. We were enjoying a mutual endorphin-rush of shared purpose.

"If you were not so strapped for cash, how many more blind patients could you offer free surgery to?" I asked Mritunjay.

I had been into the operating theatre and had seen the slickest cataract surgery I have ever witnessed anywhere: three minutes per operation with the eyes looking practically untouched at the end. A few months later John Sandford Smith would write a report describing one of the AJEH surgeons as the "best eye surgeon I have ever come across."

"We could probably operate on about 1500 blind patients each month" said Mritunjay.

Wow! An extra 1500 blind people cured of cataract blindness every month. We simply had to fund this.

"We'll fund the next three months" I said, knowing that we had money in the bank to fulfil this commitment. But Mritunjay had been burned by false promises from foreigners in the past, so I added:

"I really mean it. And the way we work, you can have the money immediately after you have done the month's surgery and have sent me the surgical data. I have already examined many of your post-operative patients. Your surgeons are very good."

Mritunjay looked elated. And a few months later he paid me back in the best possible way that he could at that time. Hundreds of miles north of Mastichak, Dr.Helen Rao asked me to send the very last Second Sight surgeons to her eye department at Raxaul before she left. As it was a slack time at the AJEH, Mritunjay offered two of his own fantastic eye surgeons.

The temperature was 45 degrees and the visiting surgeons found a demoralised team at Raxaul, on account of Dr.Helen's imminent departure. But they all worked hard and in the department's closing day over 100 blind patients were discharged back into their communities with excellent vision. The AJEH ophthalmologists pledged their support to Dr.Helen wherever she ended up working in the future. I don't think they took their bright pink theatre gowns with them to Raxaul. But I am told there was definitely a feel-good factor at the eye department whilst they were there.

Chapter Twenty-two

Beggars in Mercedes and Protectors of Sight

We rolled up our trousers and waded into the muddy river. The small wooden boat was already over laden but that wasn't going to stop anyone, including us, from clambering on-board.

I found a small space on the floor amongst a group of women and children. They inched closer together to make more room for me. The boat rocked considerably and my nearest co-passenger leaned against me and rested her arm on my leg to steady our tightly-packed group. I noticed a bright green hospital venflon attached with tape to her hand; she had obviously been sent home from a clinic with some intravenous medication to take.

"This boat is the only passenger boat to get across to the diara, the islands in the middle of the river," said Mritunjay, perched on the side of the vessel.

"The eye patients have to come this way, too."

"I expect more than a few must have thrown up" I said. "Motion sickness is much worse when you have no sight."

"Yes probably. But that wasn't the main problem," said Mritunjay. "The main problem was that fifty per cent of the patients got lost! They boarded the boat and got off the other side. But they never made it to our bus that was waiting to pick them up at the main road. The relatives who were guiding the blind patients couldn't find the way. For some it was their first experience of leaving the diara."

"Are you serious? You mean they live their entire lives on these islands and never even go across to the other side?"

"Definitely. That was the case for many."

The isolation of this community, located just a few hours from Bihar's capital city, was confirmed when we alighted on the diara themselves. I rode pillion on a motorbike belonging to a hospital volunteer who turned out to be the owner of the only real shop. Drinking chai there, I was surrounded by women who began to talk energetically in the local dialect. They did not understand Hindi.

"You know what they are saying?" asked Mritunjay. "They are saying: from the look on her face it is as if she cannot understand a word we are saying. They know that you are a not from here but the idea that you speak a different language is new for them."

He continued: "I wanted to bring you here to show you just how cut-off some communities are in Bihar. In Mastichak, where our hospital is, there is no electricity as you have seen. So we work on 24hour generators. Here, the richest man in the entire community is the man who has the only oil lamp."

The owner of the oil-lamp, our host, the shop-owner, smiled proudly.

On the way back, we caught the cattle-boat, much more up-market than the passenger boat. It was piloted by a muscle-bound man with an elaborate twirly moustache who manoeuvred the vessel with great skill, using his right leg on the tiller and his arms to push a long pole into the river-bed. We moored at a different part of the river, at a place where much larger boats were packed with sand. And hundreds of workers moved from boat to land, carrying basket after basket of the stuff to waiting lorries.

This time the question to Mritunjay was:

"They are foreigners aren't they? So where's their hawai jahaaz (aeroplane)?"

They seemed genuinely surprised that we had arrived in a mere four-wheel drive. And very sweetly brought some water for us to wash our muddy feet.

As we waited for our jeep to arrive I stood and faced India's most sacred river, Mother Ganga, so broad and sludgy at this point in her course. Here she was a physical barrier between the people of the diara and the rest of Bihar. But I saw her also as a symbol of the huge chasm between the poor who are supposed to be the beneficiary of so many organisations, and the organisations themselves. It is almost as if there are two parallel universes.

I once had a Skype conversation with an American who describes himself as being motivated by "compassionate capitalism". With absolute conviction he had told me:

"I see no problem in asking a villager in Bihar to pay one month's salary for a cataract operation."

This was after a discussion about where Second Sight worked in India during which he amply demonstrated that he would be hard pushed to place Bihar on a map of the country. This man, who has advised some of the most high-profile NGOs in the world, seemed to be under the impression that villagers living a subsistence existence actually had the ability to save money.

I gave him every opportunity to redeem himself. Just in case he was not aware of the level of extreme poverty in the areas in which

Second Sight works (because rural Bihar is not the most visited place even for compassionate capitalists). I painted a picture of the life of just one of our patients in Bihar. I told him about Lalpari Devi, of whom I wrote earlier. I described how Lalpari's husband and three children used to have an income of 100 rupees a day (about £1.25p) which the husband earned as a cycle-rickshaw operator. However, he didn't own the cycle. And one day the owner took it back. The family income then dropped to just 20 rupees (25p a day) and a bag of rice given to Lalpari by the woman whose house she cleaned.

The compassionate capitalist was most interested in the maths: 20 rupees a day, was 140 a week, that's about 600 rupees a month. Yes, and that was about what he thought reasonable to charge for a cataract operation in India: 600 rupees. So, heh presto, a month's salary for this family was enough to pay for a cataract operation! I could almost hear him slapping his thighs in satisfaction at having proved his point.

It was such a ludicrous viewpoint it was verging on farce. So I extricated myself from the conversation in the most dignified way that I could.

"Here in Britain," I said. "The fifth richest nation in the world, we do not expect people to pay one month's salary for a cataract operation. Why on earth should we expect some of the poorest people on this planet to do so?"

Years after this infamous Skype conversation, a report came my way written by the late John Cheatham, another American but of an entirely different ilk. He was originally an investment banker but retrained as a doctor at the age of 40 (an even greater age than I was when I went to medical school). Like me, he had had a life-changing experience during his first career. A banking trip had taken him to Brazil where he had witnessed the cataract operation of a poor blind woman. He was deeply affected by how her life had changed once her sight was restored. So he became an ophthalmologist and worked entirely in developing countries. He died aged only 64.

He wrote of his astonishment at the attitude common amongst representatives of international NGOs involved in global blindness.

"They tend to look upon the poor in an adversarial and suspicious fashion i.e. that these patients are 'trying to get something for nothing' — a little of the 'beggar in the Mercedes' syndrome. They see little inconsistency in pushing for financial sacrifices on the part of the poor and then, supported by donor funds, heading for the airport to attend a conference in the comfort and affluence of a luxury hotel."

In the same vein, on my very first visit to India for Second Sight, I was told by a group of Delhi ophthalmologists that the blind only "appreciate" cataract surgery if they have contributed towards its cost. Foreign NGOs use even more absurd language: they talk about patients "participating in their treatment." Have any of these people even talked to a patient made blind by cataract? If they had they would know that actually the eye surgery itself is the easy bit. Even with fabulous hospital teams like the AJEH doing their best to minimise upheaval and fear for village patients, the blind nevertheless have to make a huge effort to reach hospital for their surgery and they are forced to trust so many total strangers. Is this not enough participation in return for the precious gift of sight?

It is easy to see how John Cheatham concluded his report with the words:

"Ophthalmology is very close to being dominated by people for whom reaching the blind in a more efficient, higher volume manner is not a principal motivating factor."

His report advises against attempting to change the minds of such people. But it is so so tempting to continue to believe that at heart they really do want to cure the blind. Especially if you are an incorrigible optimist like me. Which is probably why, every time yet another organisation plumps for "curing unnecessary blindness" as their goal, I still feel a sense of hope.

A big corporate bank active in India launched its Seeing is Believing project a few years ago, matching employees' donations with bank donations. Millions of dollars have been raised and it has been awarded for being an excellent example of public-private-partnership. I was put in touch with one of their British representatives, who had actually taken the trouble to visit India, and even to visit the state of Bihar! We exchanged emails and I encouraged her to fund rural hospitals as 80% of Bihar's blind people lived in the countryside.

She told me that the bank had decided to stick to "urban projects" because this approach "seemed appropriate" for the bank because its branches were in cities. In addition, she wrote, a UN report stated that 50% of the *world's* population now lived in urban areas and this was likely to increase!

I got ridiculously hot and bothered and then profoundly depressed by this interchange. I should have just adopted the attitude of a mild-mannered farmer called Bunke Bimari Sigh, with whom I drank chai in a small village called Tarwa Parisia in Bihar. Bunke had been blind from cataract until his successful surgery. He then became a Protector of Sight for the Akhand Jyoti Eye Hospital. This means he has taken upon himself to help eradicate blindness from his entire taluka, comprising about 30 villages. This is his repayment to the hospital, his community and to India. Going from door to door, he regularly identifies about 50 patients a month who need treatment.

"You are as important as the eye surgeon," I had told him.

He had shrugged and smiled serenely.

"There is so much work for us all to do," he replied simply.

Chapter Twenty-three

On a war footing

Mritunjay and I poured over the map of Bihar. I had playfully started referring to his office as the War Room and of course strategic planning always requires recourse to maps. I must also admit to feeling a huge surge of excitement whenever I unfold my increasingly tatty map of Bihar; it has become a record of my countless travels through the countryside by rail, road, small boat and horse-drawn tonga. It is also a constant reminder that while I can travel the state with such relative ease, one million blind Biharis cannot even leave their homes without assistance.

The map of Bihar resembles a butterfly: its wings spread wide to the north and south, the river Ganges its spine cutting the state in almost two equal halves and two tributaries of the Ganges making the antennae pointing west into the neighbouring state of Uttar Pradesh. Running along the edges of the butterfly's right wing is Nepal and the Indian state of Jharkhand nudges its left wing. West Bengal lies at the 'feet' of the butterfly.

The Bihar Government's website is usually an accurate source of information about the state. From the statistics about the number of hospitals in each district you can get a good idea of what you are going to find on the ground when you visit these areas. For example, the north western districts of Paschim, Champaran, Gopalganj, Purba, and Sitamarhi are recorded as having no government hospitals or clinics at all. That was why the Eye Department at The Duncan Hospital at Raxaul in West Champaran had been crammed with blind patients and Second Sight surgeons restored sight to over 15,000 people there.

The Akhand Jyoti Hospital, the AJEH, has it main base hundred of miles south of Raxaul, at Mastichak. But Mritunjay was telling me about plans for three other satellite hospitals at locations in western Bihar so that the whole of this part of the state could be covered. He would leave the south-western districts of Rohtas, Bhabua, Aurangabad and Gaya to Gems, the Second Sight partner hospital at Sikaria. The Eye Department at Gems was now run by Dr.Helen Rao.

Mritunjay and I puzzled over the eastern part of Bihar. Some intriguing stats had drawn me to visit this area. Purnia district was recorded as having as many as 16 hospitals and yet its population was far lower than the north-western districts.

When I had visited Purnea I found almost every road lined by signs proclaiming the names and specialties of doctors, from general surgeons, to dermatologists to obstetricians. If buildings were not clinics, they were pharmacies with shelves crammed with tablets, bottles of drops, bandages and syringes. You can drive around the five kilometres of Purnia in no time at all and no part of the town is over populated by Indian standards. One must assume then that this is must be one of the most over-medicated, over-treated sections of Indian society. How else do all those pharmacies and doctors make such a comfortable living? This was a Private Practise Haven in the heart of India's poorest state.

I had made contact with almost every one of the 12 ophthalmologists in Purnia, either meeting in person or speaking over the phone. All were in private practise. They appeared to work in isolation. None had considered banding together to start up a charitable hospital to tackle cataract blindness amongst the town patients unable to pay. The idea of running outreach programmes into the surrounding villages to find and treat the blind was met with utter surprise.

One ophthalmologist told me, sipping his whiskey: "Actually none of us doctors really go outside the home after dark. There is always a danger of kidnap."

The government hospital was appalling. Filthy. In the operating theatre used once in a while by the resident ophthalmologist the eye-piece on the microscope hung loose, like a partially decapitated head. The ophthalmologist was a nice man and kind to the one post-operative patient who was in his consulting room when we arrived. He showed us around his sorry department and then escorted us back to the main road. On the way he spied the car of the district's Chief Medical Officer.

"Would you like to meet the CMO?" he asked in a quiet voice. "Perhaps you can ask him about my replacement microscope."

The CMO sat behind a desk piled high with papers. He was polite. I congratulated him on having a resident ophthalmologist and asked about the replacement microscope. Without even the slightest hesitation he replied:

"One is coming. A Zeiss. It will be here soon."

A Zeiss microscope is the most expensive microscope available. There was simply no way that a government hospital in Bihar was going to provide one for its eye surgeon. We all knew that he was being economical with the truth. The sad ophthalmologist dropped his eyes and his already sagging shoulders drooped further. We pretended that we believed the CMO and made our exit.

On this same trip to eastern Bihar I had also visited the town of Katihar, the home of Dr.Ajit Poddar one of the eye surgeons at the AJEH. He had a group of medical friends who dearly wished to start an eradication of blindness programme there. They were an honest, idealistic group and had already started other medical programmes in the villages around Katihar. It did seem as if Katihar could be a potential base for charitable eye work.

This is what Mritunjay and I were now discussing, peering over the map. The trouble with planning such a rapid and exponential expansion was that both the AJEH and Second Sight would have to treble their income to fund these projects. Both organisations were really planning beyond our budgets. Meanwhile, there was a huge hospital that could increase its workload overnight if those running it had the will.

Earlier that day we had visited a huge Jain hospital at a place called Rajgir, a sacred site for many Indians. The150 bedded eye hospital is far older than the AJEH and sits in a sprawling 52,000 square feet of beautiful grounds. Four of us, Mritunjay and Dr.Poddar from the AJEH and Lin Brown and myself from Second Sight had gone along one morning.

First impressions were impressive: spacious and well-kept clinics and wards and a full team of experienced ophthalmologists. We spent a considerable amount of time with one of the doctors, a man born, bred and trained in Bihar and with Mataji, the head of the organisation, a quiet woman who was probably in her seventies.

I explained that I knew of their good work in the past, of how they used to go into the villages and bring in the blind and offer them free surgery. I said that my friend Dr.Mangtoo Ram, a respected Patna ophthalmologist used to volunteer his services at Rajgir and had recommended that I speak to them as the cataract blindness problem in Bihar now needed to be tackled with some urgency. If we all pulled together we could turn the tables and make Bihar, currently the worst state, the best state for eradicating blindness. I got off my soap-box.

"I feel inspired hearing you talk," said the ophthalmologist. Mataji dropped her eyes quickly and got on with her paperwork. The doctor gave her a quick side-look then continued.

"We no longer do outreach work. We get enough walk-in patients to keep all our doctors busy."

"So that means blind patients who cannot make it to hospital, are staying blind."

"Yes," he admitted. "That is true."

Then he added:

"But if you can give some funds, then we can help you with your project."

There was a sharp intake of breath by Dr.Poddar, and Mritunjay and Lin shifted in their seats.

"Surely, doctor, as a Bihari and an ophthalmologist, the eradication of blindness is *your* concern, too," I said, voicing all our thought-bubbles.

"Yes, yes, of course," he said.

"Then all you have to do is re-start those outreach programmes," I suggested. "You have the vehicles, you have the space, and you have the staff."

"We will consider this," he said, once again giving another side-look at Mataji.

In the post-mortem over a cup of chai we decided that there was really only a fifty per cent chance that this hospital would join us in our eradication of blindness programme. This was such a pity. Like the AJEH the hospital had managed to crack the problem of recruiting and retaining ophthalmologists in rural Bihar and they were obviously doing high quality work or patients would not be flocking in. They were surrounded by a rural Bihar in which probably every village harboured some villagers needlessly blind from cataract. But they did not seem to think that they had a duty to reach them. It was very sad. It was also mildly irritating to be asked for money when they were part of an international organisation with 10 offices in 7 countries and an access to donors that neither the AJEH or Second Sight have.

"It only requires them to tweak their working pattern a little and they could reach the blind," commented Lin after the meeting. "It would not even have to cost that much more. But they have got too comfortable. They don't want to go out into the field."

Lin's words sum up a kind of laziness that is at the centre of the eradication of blindness programme in India. There is a precise and practical definition of blindness that has been internationally agreed upon. This can be assessed very easily in the field with a small vision chart or by a field worker asking people to "count fingers". The international definition is crucial: it demarcates a level of visual loss that prevents a person from walking about or navigating independently. India has upwards of seven million of people fitting this category and it costs the country $2billion each year. Curing cataract blindness means reaching these people.

Of course, it is far easier for beneficiaries of international funds to just take the money, offer free surgery to any poor patient with cataract and never organise outreach programmes to specifically reach those completely blind from the same condition. So more blind people join the backlog each year. And the problem gets worse not better, in spite of the injection of funds. Many donors are ignorant of these facts.

I found a way, however, to highlight this crucial point with our main financial donor-organisation, the Savitri Waney Charitable Trust.

I brought Rebecca Peltenburg, the Trust's Manager, to the AJEH. She had the full tour and was suitably impressed. Savitri had for years been contributing money to surgery carried out by our volunteer surgeons. I now wanted them to fund surgery carried out by the resident surgeons at the AJEH. The Trust also funded a south Indian hospital. So I encouraged Rebecca to find out how many blind patients this south Indian hospital saw each week. She checked and discovered that, while they offered free surgery to thousands of patients each year, on average only one patient a week fitted the blindness category! As by this time the AJEH were curing 100 blind people **every day** Rebecca had good ammunition with which to successfully convince her Trust to increase our funding. I think that we all felt we were entering the new decade with a renewed sense of purpose.

Chapter Twenty-four

Football is life

It was my third trip in six months to the Akhand Jyoti Eye Hospital at Mastichak. We turned off the main road from Patna at the familiar metal sign saying Parsa, then bumped along the narrow, winding, dirt-track that led to the hospital. We passed the familiar wheat fields and small hamlets, the high walls of a site earmarked for a factory and then, just before entering the village itself we saw the well-kept smallish mosque with its calming pale blue walls and elegant minarets. Next door to the mosque is the Muslim girls' secondary school. And bang next door to the school is the football pitch.

"Ah, tomorrow is Sunday," I said to Mritunjay. "I normally play football on a Sunday morning."

I knew that Mritunjay, too, was passionate about football, although more willing to watch rather than play the game these days on account of a back injury. He turned around in the front seat to face me.

"In that case, would you like to play with the Muslim girls? They are rather keen around here," he replied.

"But you will have to get up early as they start at 6am" he added.

The next morning we were woken as usual by the priest's amplified chanting and the tinkling of bells in our temple-accommodation. The building had housed the original eye hospital. Once the purpose-built modern hospital building was ready, the temple reverted back to its proper role. Guests now stay in the rooms once providing doctors' accommodation.

Instead of pushing my ear-plugs deeper into my ears and cowering under the pillow to get an extra few minutes sleep, I was up in a thrice. A gulp of tea and a banana for sustenance and we were off.

When we arrived at the football pitch the mist was rising from the fields and the sun was still low in the sky behind the palm trees. A few men and boys were having a game but when a white Ambassador car pulled up at the edge of the pitch, they stopped and watched. Half a dozen girls got out and the driver, a man with a big smile, greeted Mritunjay.Two of the girls wore full football gear, including shin-pads and boots; one wore traditional salwar kameez and had bare feet. The driver who turned out to be the coach, Bhism Kumar Singh, was wrapped up in a warm jumper but white trainers peeped out from under his over-long trousers. Introductions were made and then we began to play, the village men and boys having promptly and courteously vacated the pitch.

Fourteen year-old Chandni, with her Bihar team-shirt played hard and seriously, tiny Madhu with a natural flair. Shabnam and Pooja tackled with conviction. Bare-footed Seema started tentatively and then stepped up her play when she realised that even without boots her kicks were strong and accurate. Mritunjay, against physiotherapist-orders, could not resist joining in. Mukesh and Azhar were already playing hard.

I ran around like a maniac. After weeks of sitting for hours on end in jeeps travelling to remote locations, or crouched over slit-lamps examining eye patients, it was just wonderful to be dashing around in the open. And playing my favourite game! I was in heaven. Seeing how keen I was coach Bhism shouted from the sidelines, telling the girls to buck up a bit, find a space, tackle, all the usual sideline dictats. Lin stood behind the goal posts and took photographs on her mobile phone.

"We *must* get that girl some proper football boots" she muttered as Seema's toes barely missed being trampled by my trainers.

Perhaps it was the sight of Seema doing her best to play in inappropriate clothing but I had a flashback to my first school days in Britain after we had moved from India. I saw my 8year-old self, dressed in striped cotton school-dress battling it out in the playground in Twickenham, joining in some improvised game vaguely related to basket-ball, the dress getting more and more ragged as the game got rougher. I was the only girl joining in; the rest stood on the sidelines looking fainting embarrassed. I didn't care though. I was having so much fun. I have never understood why the others girls did not wish to join in.

Now here I was playing football with a bunch of Muslim girls in an area of India rumoured to be the most conservative and illiterate region in the country. And how easily I could understand their pleasure and total absorption in their sport. Not for one moment did they act self-consciously or appear inhibited by the crowd, which was growing by the moment. It was positively exhilarating.

Villagers squatted on the grass or leaned on bikes; an elderly woman carrying long sticks on her head and holding the hand of a small child, stopped for a few moments then went on her way, her expression unchanging; a bus passed and tooted its horn.

After about an hour, we stopped. I asked some of the male spectators what they thought of the girls' play.

"They say that they play well" said Mritunjay, translating their local language, Bhojpuri. Beaming, he added: "And they do play well, don't you think?"

"We have got to get them some boots" muttered Lin, ever the concerned mother and grandmother.

Boots in mind, I emailed my old friend and former colleague Simon Barnes. He writes a regular sports column in the London Times and has a feel for the odd, the quirky, the inspiring tale that widens the dimension of sport. This would be right up his street.

Simon knew that I had taken up playing football at the age of 40 having been introduced to the Beautiful Game by my daughter Leyla who was then a key member of her league-winning primary school team. He knew that, even in cricket-mad India, I would always attempt to get a game in at one of our partner hospitals. He would understand the sheer joy of that early morning game in Mastichak. And he could get us some boots.

Simon wrote the briefest of pieces in his column, placed alongside a picture of bare-footed Seema with the ball in mid-air. There was a terrific response, including, to Mritunjay's delight, an email from the team doctor for Chelsea FC, his favourite English team. Donated football boots poured in, also, thankfully, some donations for the eye hospital. But the story did not end there. What occurred during the next five months was nothing less than remarkable.

Chapter Twenty-five

Thinking outside the box

Sushma's outfit was almost like a beacon in the gloom of the small hut. She wore a bright yellow, sequined salwar kameez and had a glittering bindi in the middle of her forehead that twinkled each time she moved her head. Her feet were pushed into a pair of rather uncomfortable looking patent leather sandals with small heels. She looked far older than her 14years. But she was shy, and preferred Dad to do the talking.

He told us that he earned a living from a small rice-field. He had married his wife when she was only 14, the same age as Sushma was then. His wife had had little formal education. He had fully intended to marry off Sushma at the same age: they could not afford to pay for her schooling and thought this was the best for her. But his child had begged to join the football project at Mastichak. And when the hospital people had explained to him the full extent of this scheme, he had cancelled the marriage and given his whole-hearted support.

Sushma smiled. Sitting behind her, coach Bhishm Kumar Singh, who had played a crucial part in these negotiations, sighed with a kind of tired satisfaction.

Two bottles of cold Thumbs Up were passed into the room from the shadows behind. A female face smiled at me. We drank up quickly knowing that if we stayed longer they would feel they would have to offer more food and drink. This was rural Bihar where people lived well below the poverty line and yet would go without themselves to be generous to visitors.

Sushma led us back to the road, picking her way daintily through the muddy lanes between the conglomerations of small huts where families lived cheek by jowl with their neighbours in the village of Pirari Deh. A few young men eyed her up in an interested way.

Back in the jeep I remarked to Mukesh Tiwary, Mritunjay's brother: "When they're on the football pitch, they look like children. Then you see them dressed in their normal clothes and they look like women."

"That's right," he replied. "In rural Bihar, most girls go from childhood straight into womanhood. There is no youth. What we have done is to introduce youth."

What Sushma's family had signed up to was not merely the introduction of youth into their daughter's life. The Mastichak football project turned out to be far more extra-ordinary than that and an example of the most inspired piece of lateral thinking.

Mritunjay and I had spoken frequently over the phone or on Skype during the five months since my last visit. He had hinted at some grand scheme to build on the enthusiasm of local girls for football. He had also alluded to a remark that I had made at the eye hospital that had temporarily silenced him at the time (an unusual occurrence) and had troubled him for days after.

"How come you only have one woman working at the hospital?" I had asked.

The one woman in question had spent about fifteen minutes with me, holding my hand and babbling away in Bhojpuri, the local language I did not understand, obviously just delighted to have some female company.

Mriunjay's response at the time was that local women did not come forward for jobs at the hospital because so few had completed their schooling. But you could tell that he did not really feel that this was a good enough excuse.

"You have a way of saying something that plants an idea in my head" said Mritunjay over Skype a few weeks later. "I think you will be encouraged by what you see when you are here next."

And what a prophetic understatement that turned out to be.

When I returned five months later and went to play football one morning, I found the Mastichak pitch teeming. Over 60 girls, Muslims as well as Hindus from every caste, were dressed in smart blue or yellow kit and were being put through some rigorous training. Some had arrived on cycles, others on foot, and many had been transported there by the hospital bus normally used for patient transportation.

A woman in her late 20s wearing tracksuit bottoms and a T-shirt, was organising the large group into different training routines. Her long hair was tied back in one tidy, thick plait. Madhu Singh, a member of the Bihar State Women's Team and the first Bihari to make it to the national squad, waved at us but did not break off from her coaching.

On the far side of the pitch were a few stragglers, either girls who had not come with the proper kit and so were not allowed to take part in the formal training, or some younger girls who had not yet been accepted onto the scheme. Bhism Kumar Singh was also in this group and I slunk off to join them and played as energetically as I could in the March heat. But I was itching to hear the full story. How had a small group of Muslim girls become what appeared to be a fully fledged Football Academy in the heart of rural Bihar?

When the girls took a break, Mritunjay introduced me to Madhu who gave me the same single-minded concentration that she had earlier given to the girls. She understood English but preferred to reply to my questions in Hindi. Now 27years-old, Madhu came from a poor family, the main family bread-winner being her brother who had his own chai stall. She had started playing football at the age of 16 and her family had encouraged her from the start. When she made it to the State team they were pleased; when she got into the national team they were over the moon. Madhu stressed that her family recognized that through football she had learned discipline and had grown in confidence. It wasn't just about getting into good teams she said, it was both sport and an approach to Life. She hoped that she would be able to instil this into the Mastichak girls.

Such a wise outlook has stood Madhu in good stead and prevented her from becoming bitter about her own predicament prior to her Mastichak appointment. Representing her country had not improved her socio-economic status. When not playing matches all over the country and occasionally abroad, she was expected to fend for herself; female football players in India are not given any help financially. However, as most, unlike Madhu, come from better-off backgrounds, they can usually manage.

An Indian current affairs magazine had highlighted Madhu's plight: how could someone who had represented her country in sport be allowed to continue in poverty, they had demanded. The government promised to provide her with a job. It did not materialise. So Mritunjay went one step further. He offered Madhu not just a job but a Dream Job: coaching girls from similar backgrounds to herself, all from rural Bihar.

"I wanted to do this properly," he said. "Organised football training, regularly and aiming high. Madhu was the perfect choice for a coach. But there was something else that worried me. It all started with the girls' enthusiasm for the game. But where would that lead if they were pulled out of school and married off at the age of just 14 years, which is typical in this area. So first we scouted around for talent. Then, having identified keen players, we spoke to the families of very single one of them. We offered them a deal. If they agreed not to marry off their girls until at least the age of 21, the hospital would pay for their schooling at the local government institutions as well as their football training at Mastichak four mornings a week."

As poverty was the main reason behind the child-marriages, most families agreed to take up his offer. There was a small group, however, who were under the sway of the village 'rich man.' A resident in the city of Kolkata most of the time, this man had nevertheless built a six story building in the village and left it empty, a folly in the true sense of the word, but impressing some villagers.

"This man caused a bit of a problem. He told people it was wrong for the girls to be wearing shorts in public. So we went to see him and pointed out that his own daughters were living in Kolkata, wearing tight jeans and make-up and why was that alright while girls playing a sport in the proper clothing was not? Most people agreed with us and stopped objecting."

The wearing of shorts also worried the village Imam, admitted Mritunjay. Irshad Ahmed was in favour of the football-education project; after all 80 per cent of Muslims in rural Bihar lived below the poverty line. But he worried about those bare legs in public. Mritunjay suggested that they consult the Koran. They could not find anything in the Koran that ruled out the wearing of shorts whilst playing sport. The Imam was satisfied.

"Actually, he went one step further," said Mritunjay. "He asked if his own five year-old daughter could be put down on the waiting list."

The very same week that I was in Mastichak, in New Delhi there were two days of uproar in the Upper House of India's Parliament. After 13 years of stalling, the Women's Reservation Bill finally managed to clear the first political hurdle as the Upper House voted in favour. But only after venomous opposition. In addition, there is no guarantee that the Bill, designed to give women better representation in the legislatures, will actually get passed.

Meanwhile, in a small corner of India's most impoverished and illiterate state, child-marriage dating back hundreds of years had been overturned in just five months.

As Mritunjay and I stood talking the parents of one of the footballers approached me. How had I got the idea for such a wonderful scheme that would provide a better future for his daughter, asked the father? Actually, I had just played football with the girls, the scheme was Mr.Tiwary's idea, I replied. Yes, but how did I find the energy to play football when I must work so hard as a doctor, he persisted, eager to give me credit for something. I just love the game, I replied. Just like their daughter.

The mother smiled. She could only have been in her early thirties herself. Would she have liked to play football as a girl, I asked. Definitely, she replied.

Madhu blew her whistle and there was a mass movement of girls off the pitch and into the bus, onto cycles, or walking towards the hospital. Within fifteen minutes we were all back at the AJEH. The girls traipsed past bemused patients and up the stairs to the top floor where they were given breakfast. This nutritious meal was also a well thought-out part of the football scheme as most of the girls are severely anaemic. (Seventy per cent of girls in rural Bihar suffer from anaemia). Following breakfast, they positioned themselves behind desks in an improvised classroom.

"We have started English classes," said hospital manager Azhar. "Perhaps you want to take a class? Just five minutes."

Five minutes later I asked Mritunjay why he wanted the girls to learn English. With an expression signifying something like 'here comes the best bit' he began to explain the full joined-up thinking of the football-education project, or as he had christened it, the Akhand Jyoti Football Academy.

"First you had pointed out that we had only one woman employee," he said. "Then some of my ophthalmic assistants here at the hospital started showing signs that they could be tempted away to the cities by adverts in the Press for jobs in private practise offering a lot more money. This was worrying because our work here is expanding so fast since Second Sight has been working with us."

The possible exodus of trained ophthalmic assistants was indeed a worrying and unexpected prospect. Usually in remote rural areas, it is the eye surgeons who are difficult to retain. (That was why I had stared Second Sight in the very first place.) But the AJEH was the first hospital I had come across in rural Bihar that had managed to crack this particular problem. In fact there was a waiting list of ophthalmologists hoping to work there. But no hospital can do without enough ophthalmic assistants. They are the people who go out into the field to run diagnostic camps, screen patients for surgery and refract them to see if they need glasses. Ophthalmic assistants also carry out all the pre-operative tests on surgical patients and act as scrub nurses in the operating theatre. It was no wonder that Mritunjay was concerned about looming staff shortages.

Looking around the classroom full of bright-eyed, bushy-tailed girls, I saw where this was leading.

"That explains the English and IT classes," I said.

"Yes. If these girls complete their schooling, have some knowledge of English and computing, then we can train them up to become ophthalmic assistants. And they are far less likely to want to run off to the cities to work. They will want to stay near their villages. Now everyone benefits. The girls have the chance of a guaranteed job and a career, their families will have more money. And our eye hospital gets staff."

"And no more child marriage."

"Yes, and no child marriage."

Ophthalmic assistants cannot, however, be trained overnight. And, for the AJEH to escape criticism about not having formally trained staff, Mritunjay had decided to apply for Government permission to run a fully recognized course. As anything connected with the Bihar Government can get mired in bureaucracy and corruption, he expected this to take some time. To his astonishment, when the inspectors visited the AJEH they were so amazed at the scale of the work and the obvious need for a good eye hospital in that area, that they granted permission for the course. The only snag was that they said that the course had to begin that very July. It was then March. I now realised why he had said so often over the phone that "everything is happening so fast."

I saw what I had to do. The doctors and refractionists at the AJEH were already over-worked keeping up with the huge patient work-load. In the immediate future, they would never be able to take on the main teaching and training for the ophthalmic technicians' course. But I now had a database of nearly 100 eye surgeons willing to offer their time to Second Sight. Would any of these ophthalmologists swap their surgical hats for their lecturing hats?

As I was mulling over this we were called away to take a look at the new operating theatre under construction. It would be housed in an extra floor, the fifth, on an existing building. It was going up at lightening speed.

"You don't waste time, do you Mritunjay," I said.

"Well you see, we have to get on with it. If the girls are going to be taken onto the Ophthalmic Technicians course, they will need a hostel within the hospital. I cannot expect them to make their way here every day from their far-flung villages."

Gesturing around the already crammed hospital grounds, he added:

"The only place to build the hostel is up there. On top of the operating theatre."

We seemed to be aiming for the sky in every sense of the phrase.

Chapter Twenty-six

Orissan Odyssey

Orissa

Just when I had convinced my trustees that we should put all our efforts into eradicating blindness in Bihar, cries of help from another neglected and volatile area began to grow more persistent. As by now we had established a reputation as an organisation dedicated to finding the blind in forgotten areas of India, it was hard to ignore these appeals.

Orissa lies to the south-west of Bihar. On the map it looks to me like a flying fox, head in the north and contained in its short stumpy tail the areas of Koraput and Malkangiri districts surrounded by the state of Andhra Pradesh to the east and Chhattisgarh to the west. Nearly a quarter of Orissa's population are tribal communities. And Christian missionaries have always been active there. Like Nancy and Virendra Henry.

When I first met the Henrys they were energetic, independent septuagenarians, Dr.Henry still practising as a general surgeon and Nancy as a nurse-advisor and trainer.

They had met very young, when Nancy had left her native America to work as a missionary in India. She had learned the language Oriya in her first year in the country and is now more fluent than her Indian-born husband.

Nancy is small, fair with sparkling light eyes; Virendra a solidly-built man with the lugubrious features of a hound-dog. They call each other Mama and Papa and are one of the most devoted couples I have ever met.

Their family house is at Tilda in the state of Chhattisgarh where Virendra was born. But, when I first met them, they were travelling once a month to Orissa, so that Virendra could provide general surgery for patients at a struggling mission hospital at Diptipur. This hospital had a full team of ophthalmic assistants but no ophthalmologist and had pleaded with us to send Second Sight eye surgeons.

The journeys from Tilda would start out at the crack of dawn after the Henrys had carefully packed their old Ford with all that we needed, including plenty of good music cassettes to entertain us on the way. On one occasion, my 22year-old daughter Leyla and I sat in the back seat with a rifle pointing at us from between the front seats.

"Papa used to hunt a lot," explained Nancy. "But don't worry, the rifle isn't loaded. We are taking it to be repaired. If we pass any police-wallahs just throw a shawl over it."

Orissa is known as the Temple State of India. And certainly temples are what draw tourists to eastern Orissa with its coastline of unspoilt sandy beaches, easily reached from the well-serviced capital city of Bhubaneswar. They come to witness extra-ordinary events like the Puri Juggernaut Festival when Hindu devotees pull an enormous carriage through the streets at great risk to themselves and to bystanders. The Konark Dance Festival also draws thousands of tourists each year who watch classical Indian dance in the spectacular setting of the ancient Temple of the Sun. Dancer-Leyla had accompanied me to Orissa to attend this festival.

Western Orissa is another world. In Virendra Henry's youth it was covered by thick forests in which he would hunt every evening after work. The forests are still there but under grave threat from greedy mining companies who pay little heed to environmental damage and less attention to the upheaval their work causes when tribal communities are forced to relocate. In these areas live most of Orissa's 62 tribes. Together with the high number of what Indians refer to as "scheduled castes", nearly 40 per cent of Orissa's population is made up of India's most deprived communities. It has been estimated that over 55% of rural people live on less than 12 rupees a day.

These are the facts. But in spite of them, Orissa is not at all a depressing place. Particularly when viewed from the back of an old Ford driven by a couple who know the countryside like the back of their hand and who share a great love for the place and its people.

For most of their working lives, the Henrys had run a highly successful mission hospital at Bissam Cuttack. Bissam Cuttack means Poisoned Air. Malaria is endemic there. It is also in the district of Koraput where Maoists groups are active. These groups are usually referred to as Naxalites named after a farmers' uprising against landlords in a place called Naxal in West Bengal in 1967. More than thirty years later, the Naxalites have control over large swathes of rural India and are locked in confrontation with those they see as representatives of the Indian State.

Government ministers now refer to the Naxalites as India's "most serious security threat."

In all their time at Bissam Cuttack, however, the Henrys and other missionary-medics were able to co-exist with communists and their sympathisers because they simply got on with the job of providing health-care for everyone in the community, including the most neglected. As a result the Henrys are fairly sanguine about many situations where others see potential dangers.

In the summer of 2008, anti-Christian violence erupted in Orissa. The state has a sorry history of such senseless violence, the most appalling incident being that of Graham Staines, an Australian missionary who was murdered with his two young sons as they slept in their vehicle after visiting a local festival in 1999.

This time the trouble had started not far from Diptipur Hospital where a Second Sight eye surgeon was operating. An influential Hindu priest was murdered. A group opposed to the swami's somewhat intolerant policies decided they could not tolerate him. The group took full responsibility for the murder. It made no difference. If there is any death or dispute in Orissa, the thugs who are always there, waiting for an opportunity to create havoc, emerge in their full-grown ugliness…and pick on Christians.

Dr.Henry's view was that the eye work could go on.

"They never touch the hospitals," he told me in his deep, slow drawl. "We should continue the eye work."

But he did advise one piece of caution: send only Indian Second Sight surgeons rather than foreign-looking doctors who would draw the attention of trouble-makers. This meant cancelling the planned trip of John Sandford Smith and replacing him with Dr.Jacob Koshy from Hyderabad. John was understanding, Jacob unbothered as he had been to Diptipur many times.

The police were not as relaxed as Dr.Henry, however. They warned that Diptipur Hospital could be a target for violence and ten police officers from the Central Guards set up camp on the hospital's sprawling compound.

Initially, Diptipur's only resident doctor, 27 year-old Dr.Ipsita, went into hiding, venturing into the hospital at night when the police alerted her that an emergency patient had come in. This was usually a woman in the late stages of a problematic pregnancy needing a caesarean section.

"It was a bit scary at first, going at night-time" she told me over the phone. "But once you have done it, it's not so bad. Now I don't mind."

When Ipsita deemed it safe to man the hospital during the day, Dr.Jacob returned to Diptipur to operate on patients with cataract. He restored sight to 223 people. Some of these were tribal patients who had been camping deep in the forests, afraid that thugs would accuse them of having converted to Christianity. When they had heard the news that the eye work at Diptipur had re-started, their relatives took the risk and brought them in for surgery.

Ipsita emailed me.

"I want to inform you that there are 10 policemen sent from the Central Guards still camping on our compound to protect us, but the tension that caused us such fear is no longer felt and the camp went on smoothly for all."

I visited Diptipur just after this and found an extraordinarily calm and relaxed young doctor, living in the doctor's bungalow with a cook as her only companion. All the nurses and paramedics lived in villages sprinkled around the hospital.

"It's amazing Ipsita" I said. "When I first came here there were three doctors, and you were the timid quiet one. Now they have all gone. And you are holding the fort all on your own in difficult times. Isn't it lonely?"

"Mmm.Sometimes," she admitted. "Mostly I miss Dr.Rajnish's dog."

She laughed and shrugged.

"But the work is good. And the patients are there."

As long as Nancy and Virendra Henry were available to Dr.Ipsita for advice, moral and practical support, and as long as they could travel to Diptipur to help organise the eye camps, we sent eye surgeons. Computer-literate Nancy was very prompt with sending on the surgical results so essential for our records and for self-auditing.

Then tragedy struck. Breaking a habit of a life-time, the Henrys decided against driving themselves cross-country and took a train. Disembarking at their destination, Virendra stepped down onto the platform and turned round to give Nancy his hand. She slipped and fell in the gap between the carriage and the platform. Her injuries were severe. A few weeks later Virendra had a stroke. Months of hospitalisation and slow recovery followed.

Now Diptipur Hospital's future was truly precarious. But having started work in western Orissa we knew that this area of this state had a blindness problem that rivalled even that of rural

Bihar. I had no knowledge of any other rural charitable hospital in western Orissa other than Diptipur that was capable of being used as a base for our Second Sight surgeons.

Luckily, I was the recipient of an email that proved wonderfully serendipitous.

Chapter Twenty-seven

Third eye

Sambalpur, Orissa

"What is your objective analysis of my team?" asked Dr.Shiva Prasad Sahoo, leaning earnestly across the desk in the small office of the Trilochan Netralaya Eye Hospital.

"Well, they're very enthusiastic, dedicated,idealistic…"

"Anything else?"

I caught Francisca's eye and knew we were thinking the same thing.

"They all look about 10years-old," I said.

"Yes," said Dr.Shiva laughing. "Except for the eye surgeons, the team at the Trilochan Netralaya are very young, most are under the age of 30."

"You don't have to be young to have those qualities" I said, ever one to sniff out any hint of ageism.

"Oh, my meaning is not that" said Shiva quickly. "But when they are young, it is easier to bend their personalities. They are not set in their ways. They can be motivated to help others."

As he said this, the 34year-old handsome doctor possessed with a smile that can light up a room, looked as if he had the weight of the world on his shoulders. For a moment I felt as if I were talking to an old man. As it turned out, Dr.Shiva does have a huge burden of responsibility, albeit it one that is self-imposed because he is chasing a dream.

In the midst of the dilemma over what to do about Diptipur Hospital, I had received an email sent out to a host of different people by a man who worked for an Irish-based charity and was himself from the state of Orissa. The gist of the mail was this: a dynamic young team working out of a rented building had cured over 4,500 blind people in six months. The team were based at Sambalpur. The hospital was the Trilochan (translated as 'having three eyes') Netralaya Hospital headed by Dr.Shiva, named after the Hindu god said to be possessed of an extra inner eye. The TN team wanted to eradicate reversible blindness from Orissa.

A few months later, together with Francisca Van Holthoon, a loyal donor and friend of Second Sight, I visited Sambalpur. We were greeted at 3am at the railway station by two smiling young men clutching bouquets of flowers. They ran towards us on the platform holding the bouquets before them, for all the world like that slow-motion Timotei shampoo advert when a young man sees a girl he fancies, buys a bunch of flowers and dashes after her to thrust them into her hands. It reduced us to almost hysterical laughter as we were already suffering from severe sleep-deprivation. Our two greeters turned out to be Judhisthra, the chief refractionist at the hospital and Manoj Rath, an ophthalmic assistant. They deposited us at our hotel.

Six hours later, still groggy from lack of sleep, we were at the Trilochan Netralaya Hospital. Garlands and more flowers were presented, this time by a giggly young woman called Itty, the receptionist-cum-counsellor as she described herself and "my best employee" as Dr.Shiva described her. We met all members of the "dynamic young team" as described in the email. Their achievements seemed even more impressive when we saw the cramped premises from which they worked, barely more than a semi-detached house in a back-street of Sambalpur town. The rooms were spotless, however, and all records meticulously kept.

I examined some pre-operative patients brought in from the villages and then some post-operative paying patients. The staff stood around beaming. We were the hospital's first foreign visitors. Then we retired to the office for tea.

"So where do you live, Shiva," asked Francisca."Is your home close to the hospital?"

He smiled and dropped his eyes.

"Actually, you may not believe it. But I sleep where you are now sitting. On the floor in this office. It is perfectly fine. I sleep from midnight till 4.30 am only. "

And then we heard the whole story.

Shiva is the youngest of a poor rural family. Against all odds and with the help of scholarships, he qualified as a doctor and then specialised in Ophthalmology. He decided that as Orissa had a terrible backlog of people unnecessarily blind from reversible causes like cataract, he should build up a team that would not rest until this problem was eradicated.

Many of his staff were working at another hospital run by an NGO and where Dr.Shiva used to work. When they learned that

Shiva was establishing his own premises, they came across to him one by one, taking cuts in salary just to work with him and towards a very specific aim. They bought into his dream.

As we talked a young man came in to ask Shiva when he would start operating.

"This is Tarani," introduced Shiva. "He is 18years-old. At the other hospital he used to be the cook. But I noticed that he was not spending much time in the kitchen. Any chance he had and he would happily come to help with patients' dressings or to learn how to put the eye drops. So at TN we have trained him to assist in the operating theatre. Now he is very good."

We went to see the Operating Theatre, a small, sparse room with just one microscope and two operating tables. In the room next door, there was a shrine, containing pictures of the Pondicherry sages Sri Aurobindo and The Mother, a statue of the god Ganapati and a picture of Jesus. Dr.Shiva prays at this shrine before each theatre session.

The TN premises were similar to private clinics I had seen in many cities and towns, when ophthalmologists see a handful of patients each day and operate on even fewer. But over 4,500 patients had passed through these rooms; the vast majority had been extremely poor people brought in from the villages and who had received their surgery free of cost.

We had come with a slightly ulterior motive. I was hoping that Shiva could be a Second Sight surgeon and perhaps go to Diptipur to operate from time to time. Diptipur was only about five hours by road. It was very clear, however, that he was totally overcommitted. Apart from the work at the base hospital at Sambalpur, the team were going into many other districts and carrying out cataract surgery to reduce the backlog of blind people.

There was a certain naivety about their approach. They did the work, stumping up for all the costs and travelling huge distances by public transport to carry out the surgery at mostly government hospitals. This enabled the government to show statistics that proved they were doing something to tackle cataract blindness. The agreement was that the TN would then receive the government subsidy for these operations, to cover their costs. The money inevitably came late and never in full. Yet the TN team continued with the work, driven on by the sight of hundreds of blind patients queuing up to see them wherever they went. This after all was making an impact on Orissa's cataract blindness problem. A handful of teams working with equal diligence could restore sight to every single blind person in the state.

The stress, however, was taking its toll, admitted Shiva. The summer before, he had ended up with no money to pay his young staff. Thinking on his feet, he went into all the big businesses in Sambalpur, offered the staff free eye tests and refraction to see if they needed glasses and then charged for the spectacles themselves. As he had bought these wholesale and cheaply, he earned enough money to pay his loyal staff.

"Have you applied to any of the big NGOs for funding?" I asked.

"Oh, yes," replied Shiva. "All of them. They have all refused. They say they have no funds for new projects."

Images of wasted resources surged before my eyes. I remembered the argon laser foisted onto the Shree Bhairav Eye Hospital in rural Rajasthan in a year when international charities seemed to have collectively decided that hospitals should be encouraged to treat Diabetic Eye Disease. I had been present when Rajmal Jain had made a phone-call to ask the donating agency if his hospital could be provided with ten replacement cataract surgical sets instead; there was not much diabetic eye disease in rural Rajasthan and also his doctors were not trained to use the machine. The NGO had refused saying that lasers were being given that year. The following year expensive fundus cameras were donated, once again, for the diagnosis of diabetic eye disease.

I remembered a visual field analyser still sitting in its box at an eye hospital in the state of Jharkhand which had no ophthalmologist specialising in Glaucoma. No doubt Glaucoma was the preferred eye condition for that year for which funding was available. Of course there is nothing wrong with encouraging hospitals to treat other eye conditions that can cause blindness. But not with a blanket provision of equipment that they cannot make use of. And not if it means turning down teams at the forefront of eradicating cataract blindness which is still the main reason why millions are unnecessarily blind. But these thoughts were not helpful. What practical help could we offer Shiva?

"Dr.Lucy, one more thing," said Shiva, calling to office administrator Shibani to bring a map of the area. Spreading out the map before us he pointed down to the south-west of Orissa, that finger of land sandwiched between Andhra Pradesh and Chhattisgarh states.

"You mentioned your friends Dr.Henry and his wife. They were working here in Koraput district. This is completely a Naxalite area. I very much want to go there because definitely there will be many blind people there."

He paused. Then continued.

"What do you think? I am thinking that until they know us, there is a risk. I travel by public bus. If the Naxailites decide to shoot up a bus, then pop, that's the end of me."

I cannot remember what I muttered in reply. In any event, within nine months we were all in Naxalite country.

Chapter Twenty-eight

In Naxalite country

Western Orissa

I had expected the Central Reserve Police to be everywhere. A group had been ambushed and killed the week before and so a show of strength was likely. I had not expected that our first view of them would be quite like this : a long straggly line of runners, so varying in size that they reminded me of boys in their first year at secondary school when some have had growth spurts and others not, resulting in giants towering over others half their size. In this case they just reflected India's amazing range of stature depending on which part of the country you hailed from or how much nourishment you had had as a child.

They were all carrying guns, horizontally, but some had shed their khaki shirts and others had scarves wrapped round their heads to protect them from the hot sun. They were taking part in a 20 kilometre training course. And some were hurting.

At the bend in the forest road, their commanding officer sat in a plastic chair, supping chai, a broad-brimmed hat on his head. Seeing our vehicle, he beamed and gave us an enormous half-circle wave as we passed.

We had begun the journey at 5am in Raipur, the capital city of Chhattisgarh, rewarded for our early start by the most glorious sunrise tingeing the edges of an almost choreographed arrangement of differing sized cumuli clouds. We headed east towards Orissa and by the time we came across the running police officers were deep in the heart of Naxalite country. There were few vehicles on the road. The odd jeep, the odd public bus. When the car's engine was switched off, the forest sounds were loud.

It is estimated that about a third of India is under the control of Naxalite groups. Their strongholds and popular support are said to be mainly in the tribal areas of the states of Chhattisgarh, Orissa and Jharkhand. The more southern state of Andhra Pradesh also harbours many Naxalite groups. Supporters say they are fighting for the underdog, the millions of poor rural Indians, particularly tribal communities, who are simply neglected by the State. Opponents call them terrorists. If you read nothing but the mainstream Indian newspapers, you will come away terrified of the "Red Army", the dreaded "Naxal scourge".

This Press coverage keeps most Indians well away from these areas. But even the police, possibly that officer who waved to us, have mixed views about how to tackle the so-called Naxalite problem. And those who simply want to continue to provide services for the poor in these areas, cling to the belief that the more enlightened amongst the powerful will hold out against the hardening element that simply want to bomb the hell out of the area and kill as many Maoists as they can.

The Naxalite country we were driving through was the home of thousands of eye patients. And we were there to meet Dr.Shiva and the rest of the TN team. The previous night Dr.Shiva had travelled the 12hours from Sambalpur on a public bus but, worried about our comfort, had arranged for us to be picked up at Raipur so that we could travel on better roads in a hired vehicle. He knew that we would be travelling direct from London through Delhi and onto Raipur with no break.

Meanwhile the TN hospital bus went into the villages picking up patients for surgery. We were all soon to converge on Nabarangapur District Hospital where Dr.Shiva would already be operating.

With me on this trip was Annie Ablett, a friend and Second Sight supporter on her very first trip to India.

"I know that you have told me this is a troubled area," she said. "And it obviously must be with all these police around. But it feels so calm and peaceful."

I also felt calm and relaxed. In spite of having over 100,000 rupees in cash in my back-pack and travelling through allegedly one of the most dangerous places in the country. The money was for the TN team. It was the only way to fund their work as they did not yet possess a bank account that allowed them to receive foreign donations. They expected months more of grappling with bureaucrats and petty corruption before getting the relevant permission.

Travelling with us in the hired vehicle was Rakesh Pradhan in charge of the outreach programme for the TN team. 28year-old Rakesh has a master's degree in Social Work and a particular interest in tribal communities. It is he who goes into unknown areas, befriending the locals, learning their dialects and preparing the ground for the ophthalmic assistants who will come later to screen for eye problems. Rakesh loves his work.

"The tribal people are so simple, so honest. You give them one single thing and they give you their heart."

Rakesh had the opportunity to do a PhD in Barcelona, Spain. But turned it down to stay working for the TN hospital.

"How could I leave the TN? I would break Dr.Shiva's arm if I did that."

And heart I should think. The topic of Rakesh's PhD? Invisible rural and tribal children in Eye-Care.

Rakesh is also a keen dancer and we whiled away time on the journey watching a short video on his mobile phone of him in action. And very elegant it was too.

En route to Nabarangapur, we stopped off at the area hospital where there was a screening camp organised in collaboration with local medical workers. A large beaming man dressed in a brown safari suit, a magnifying loupe on his forehead and torch in hand, welcomed us effusively. This was Government Ophthalmic Assistant Mr.Ram. And he was beside himself with joy. Normally much of Mr.Ram's training goes wasted here and his job can be depressing; there are so many patients with cataract and no eye surgeon so he is constantly turning away the blind. Now the visiting TN team had arrived, he could call upon all his expertise. Looming over the tiny tribal patients he practically whooped with pleasure each time his bright torch shone into an eye and revealed mature cataract; with a great flourish he tore off a strip of tape and placed it firmly on the eye needing surgery. Each time he did this, he turned round to grin at us and his shoulders shook with laughter.

Perhaps it was Mr.Ram's infectious good humour but this was certainly the jolliest screening camp I had been to in rural India. And the patients themselves were so courteous to each other. One man gently led his blind wife to Mr.Ram and explained her story. She wore her bright orange sari in the typical local fashion: no choli or blouse but tied in a knot at one shoulder and worn short, at knee-length. She had one shrunken eyeball, characteristic of a long-standing non-seeing eye and white cataract in the other.

"This man has brought his Mrs" Mr.Ram told me. "He is telling that she had measles when she was young. That is why one eye has been lost. Now she can have cataract operation on other eye. They are happy."

Just then the TN's blue and white bus entered the compound, full to the brim with patients collected from villages 20kilometres away. Mahindra, the driver, a bald man built like a prize boxer and with a ready grin that displayed pan-stained red teeth, ushered them out of the vehicle and arranged them in orderly lines. They then all squatted. A grey-haired man picked his way past them leading a young girl.

"Aap ka naam kya hai?" I asked. What's your name.

"Parvati" came a big resounding voice from the small child. And then a shy smile when I said "Namaste, Parvati.".

Rakesh laughed.

"When I see young patients like this I become like Mr.Ram. Very happy" he said.

When we eventually arrived at Nabarangapur, the Government District Hospital was also swarming with eye patients and Dr.Shiva was taking a short break.

"What's the furthest these patients have come from" asked Annie as we stood in a ward filled to capacity with post-operative patients, white patches on their operated eyes.

"About one hundred and fifty kilometres," said Dr.Shiva.

"And if your team hadn't come here what would have happened to them?"

"They would remain blind," he replied. "Till they die."

In a large upstairs room, ophthalmic assistants Manoj Rath and Rabindra Sath worked their way steadily through patients, taking blood pressure, measuring the eye with keratometers and A-scans to get accurate powers for the intra-ocular lens implants. This was remote Orissa and the work-load was huge, but the pre-operative preparation was as meticulous as in a city hospital.

The next morning post-operative checks were held at 6.30am and the newly sighted patients could not wait to get home. One of them, Moonkee, an agile nonagenarian in a dazzling yellow saree, stood out from the crowd with her lithe movements and loud cackling laughter.

"Shall we go to her village?"asked Rakesh. "We can follow the bus."

We were about to jump into our vehicle when a motorbike pulled up. Two men got off, one clutching some papers.

"I think they want to speak to you," said Rakesh laughing.

It was a typical event. News spreads that a 'foreign' eye doctor is around and middle-class patients (even in Nabarangapur there are some) arrive out of nowhere to get a 'second opinion.' In this case, the patient had been seen thousands of miles away at a prestigious south Indian hospital. He had had bilateral retinal detachment and, reading the notes, had had appropriate treatment. All one can do in situations like this is reiterate that the doctors they have already seen have taken correct action. They always leave, however, a little disappointed, as if, surely, you had some magic treatment not available in India.

Now we had to catch that bus up. We took a faster route and arrived in the village of Nadapura ahead of it. Parked at the entrance to the village, we were soon surrounded by villagers.

"I am seeing so many children under the age of five years," commented Rakesh, his PhD ever on his mind.

"And there's one with a squint," I said. "Oh, and another."

"Perhaps we should do a paediatric eye camp at Nabarangapur" suggested Rakesh.

Loud hoots interrupted and the big yellow bus with 'Dharma' painted on the front, sped into the village, then stopped, jerkily, at the bend on the road.

Moonkee was almost the last to disembark, greeting us once again and then taking off at a great pace to her home. We, and the local children, had to run to keep up with her.

She turned into her compound and went immediately to wash her feet and her hands. Then she approached a young woman and baby standing outside a hut and began a ritual of pure adoration.

The child was her grandson, being seen by Moonkee for the first time, and every part of the little body had to be caressed and kissed and worshipped. Then Moonkee turned to us and blessed us, profusively, for our good work.

"I like this village,"announced Rakesh. "Shall we just stay here tonight?"

But we were booked in at the Government Circuit House and officialdom would have frowned on such spontaneous decisions.

The next morning we set off at dawn from Nabarangapur for Makangiri. A government escort vehicle was sent as this was deemed to be an even more dangerous area. I am not sure how an additional jeep and driver was going to help in the event of a problem but I suppose a back-up vehicle might come in handy if we broke down. This time Dr.Shiva was with us, laughing and joking as usual, in spite of three hours sleep.

The trees grew taller and the forests more dense.

"When the Naxalites want to call a bandh or strike, they simply cut down one of these trees and immediately the road is blocked," said Shiva.

"And has there been a strike during one of your eye camps?" asked Annie.

"Yes. And patient numbers were reduced. But we still managed to get over 400 for surgery."

"And has the TN bus ever got stopped?"

"No. Never. Even at the time of a three state strike called by the Naxalites, the TN bus was allowed to go to all the villages. They know what we are doing."

I reminded Shiva that is was not that long ago when he had been in two minds about entering Naxalite country.

"Yes there was so much talking about the Naxalites" he admitted. "But once we came here we have never had any problem from them and we don't give them any problem. They have their own enemies."

In fact, he told me, the police had brought him two Naxalite prisoners serving sentences in Malkangiri Jail. Both had traumatic cataract.

"One prisoner was a lady from Andhra Pradesh so I could not speak her language and she could not understand me" said Shiva. "But the gentleman was from Orissa so I was able to have a nice conversation with him while operating. I asked him about the accident that caused his cataract."

Shiva laughed at this point.

"He said so you don't think that when they catch us they just give us cups of tea! We get a good thrashing. Anyway, his sight was good after the operation and now he is back serving his sentence."

Let's hope the police don't thrash him again, muttered Annie.

We stopped in a small village to buy water and spotted four eye patients with their unmissable dark glasses standing waiting for the public bus. One man was delighted when he realised that Shiva was the eye surgeon who had operated on him. He wasn't a local. He was from the eastern coastal belt of Orissa but had been visiting Malkangiri for his daughter's wedding when he had heard about the eye camp. He smiled a toothy smile and praised Shiva continually.

"He is saying that his eyes are first class" said Shiva.

"Good," I replied. "Tell him that I hope his daughter's marriage proves to be first class, too."

This was translated and greeted with much laughter.

As we drove into Malkangiri Shiva pointed out the police station, surrounded by barbed wire and watch-towers. I was reminded of distant Northern Ireland during the 'troubles'.

The sombre mood did not last, though. We arrived at the building in which post-operative patients had gathered for their final, two week post-operative eye checks. And there was a party atmosphere.

Hundreds of patients sat on beds, on the floor, chatting incessantly. The din was unbelievable. Shiva immediately opened all the windows as if hoping the noise would dissipate outside. One of the few quiet people was a young girl, dressed in a yellow blouse and skirt. She was gently exploring with her hands the mattress on the bed behind her, for all the world as if she were seeing it for the first time in her life. And that was exactly the case. Eighteen year-old Lakmee, born with bilateral cataract had had the sight restored to her right eye. Dr.Shiva lifted the dark glasses from her face and she smiled shyly up at him. A white cataract, safed moti, white pearl, stared back from her left eye.

"She is having difficulty in understanding me," said Dr.Shiva laughing. "And she speaks a tribal language and I am not understanding her."

"She is from the Mau tribe," came a voice from behind.

"Ah, this is one of the interpreters," said Shiva relieved.

Through the interpreter we established that Lakmee had never gone to school. Why not? Because she was blind, replied her young mother. And now? Definitely, now she would go.

Paying great attention to this conversation was another girl, tall and dark with enormous eyes, both now free of cataract. This was 15year-old Kanan. And Kanan could not stop laughing. And ogling Dr.Shiva with great interest. She turned up later, in the consultation room, with no specific problem, but perhaps just to have another look at her handsome eye surgeon.

There were people from at least six different tribal groups amongst the patients but several interpreters on hand for communication. There was also a group of Bengali refugees, one of whom tapped me on the shoulder and spoke in perfect English. They had been settled in Orissa since the Bangla Desh War of 1960, he told me. And because they did not speak the local dialects, their villages were not given local names but numbers. His village was Number 27.

We were ushered into a small side room and offered cold drinks. Then three imposing men entered. Babu, Gautum Jain and

Rakham Jain introduced themselves in deep sonorous voices. They were local businessmen and members of the Jain community.

"Let me tell you about these gentlemen," said Shiva. "They give tremendous help but take no credit for it. Just quietly helping. During the last camp, they provided free food for all the patients. Three meals every day for three days."

Later they fed us too, with huge helping of rice and daal and vegetables and poppadums until we were bursting.

Said Gautum Jain : "It is part of our faith. To help in any way that we can."

If ever there was an event that showed all members of the community in a good light it was that Malkangiri follow-up camp. We even sat in on a government health meeting in which there were members of all the small NGOs in the area who were working in the leprosy field, including four former patients. They were moved and motivated by the visiting ophthalmic team and said they would try and mobilise eye patients for any future camps.

The only people who let the side down were two government officials, one by his presence and one by his absence: the resident ophthalmologist of whom there was no sign, and the Chief Medical Officer who requested us to come to his office. There we found him lecturing a roomful of cowed workers.

"And you," he said to me. "I understand that you are a journalist."

He must have been told that I had been videoing the entire follow-up camp and interviewing people.

"No, I am an ophthalmologist."

"Then you are the journalist?" he asked Annie.

"No, I am not."

A pause.

"So, as an ophthalmologist, what do you think of our eye work?" he said, taking credit for the TN team.

"Splendid. The TN team are well known to us," I replied.

He looked uncertain.

"Of course we have our own eye surgeon, too," he said.

"Oh, and how much operating does he do?" I asked, having already heard from local health workers that the government ophthalmologist only saw private patients.

"He does not operate much, but he is sees patients in clinic," the CMO prevaricated.

We made our excuses and left. We had a long journey back to Sambalpur.

As we made this journey, first by vehicle on an atrocious road, then by train, Shiva's mood changed dramatically. He lost the glow and light-heartedness that had been his hallmark throughout our stay in Nabarangapur and Malkangiri. He adopted a pre-occupied look, at times a deep frown, as if he were heading for a difficult meeting.

When we arrived back at the TN base it was clear why. There were unpaid bills to face, rejection letters from funders and Shiva had to brace himself for yet another humiliating meeting with the Collector of Sambalpur just to try and get him to sign a form that would allow the TN to apply for a bank account that could receive foreign donations.

The Indian Government refuse to negotiate with the Naxalites because they do not credit them with an official identity. In an odd way, back at Sambalpur, it seemed as if the small TN team had also lost their identity. Huddled in their small premises under the flyover, their extraordinary achievements in Naxalite country, curing 1,600 of Orissa's blind in just three intensive eye camps, seemed to be totally unrecognized and unrewarded. And the huge significance of medical teams bringing out the best in everybody and promoting Peace through Medicine was being completely missed.

Chapter Twenty-nine

Small heroes

"We have to support our small heroes. (Of these we have many. Many.) We have to fight specific wars in specific ways. Who knows, perhaps that's what the twenty-first century has in store for us."

Arundhati Roy

Yorkshire, England

My friend David Price, a retired dentist whom I had met at Rajmal's Shree Bairav Eye Hospital in Rajasthan, had suggested that we raise funds for Second Sight with a kind of double act. He booked the village hall in his picturesque village of Wath and invited friends.

They were a welcoming bunch and the question and answer session afterwards revealed them to be an intelligent, thoughtful and questioning group, eager to fully understand why India, a country in the headlines a great deal just then for its economic success, had such an awful problem with cataract blindness. They were particularly interested in Dr.Shiva and his young team at Sambalpur who appeared to be struggling against all odds.

A retired brigadier who had once spent time in south India found it hard to believe that the Government was doing so little. I emphasised that there were several different Indias and that rural Bihar and Orissa were a world apart from Bangalore. In the south most things worked: there were good charitable hospitals, good government hospitals, money from the National Programme for Control of Blindness managed to get distributed to the appropriate people, and there was less corruption; the population was lower and contained within smaller areas. I had already demonstrated in my talk that none of these helpful factors existed in the rural north.

"It must be so frustrating," commented a young woman barrister. "I can't understand how you can be so enthusiastic after ten years of running Second Sight. Don't you ever just feel like giving up?"

I was standing in front of the last slide in my presentation. It showed Dr.Shiva and me in the examination room at the Trilochan Netralaya Eye Hospital with two young boys.

"Let me explain why I never feel like giving up," I said turning to the slide.

"The little boy on my knee in this picture is 9year-old Subala Suna. The boy standing to attention is 12year-old Ranjit Bariha. As you can tell from their dark glasses they have both had cataract surgery. Both were born with cataract and until their parents discovered Dr.Shiva, they had no hope of ever seeing."

"In their eyes sit four intra-ocular lenses that came all the way from England. I had lugged these donated lenses, part of a big consignment, in a large suitcase, from London to Sambalpur, complaining a lot on the way. I nearly did not bring them at all. Most of the lenses were of unusual powers, suitable only for some patients and I wondered if they would be of any use. But I hated the idea that they would just go to waste if I didn't take them to India."

"I remember that when Shiva went through the lenses and discovered that he would not be able to use most of them on his hundreds of adult patients, his face had fallen a little. The IOLs were stored and almost forgotten."

"Then months later Subala and Ranjit turned up at his hospital. Shiva did the pre-operative measurements and realised that he needed some low power lenses to put into their eyes. He would have to order them specially and this would take time and be expensive. On the verge of turning away the families, he remembered my bulging suitcase of donated IOLs. A search through these found exactly the right four lenses for both Subala and Ranjit."

I told my Yorkshire audience that giving sight to blind children should not be so tenuous, so reliant on luck, on donations, on goodwill, on the dedication of eye surgeons like Dr.Shiva who worked for no salary and as hard as possible. But this was the situation as I had found it in areas of India where blindness was rampant. I had no power to change corruption, incompetence or mental laziness on the part of either government departments or international charities. But as an eye doctor I would feel negligent if I did not do my utmost to help dedicated eye teams like Dr.Shiva's.

At the end of the meeting a man called Derrick Potter approached me. Derrick is a self-made businessman, now running a highly successful logistics company.

"I am very interested in this Dr.Shiva," he said. "I would like to know how he manages, what specific things would help him. I'll start out my giving a donation. But we should meet up in London. I want to hear more. I want to help."

That Yorkshire audience reflected the mood of the country just then. The MPs expenses scandal had hit the headlines in Britain. For a few weeks, attention was also turned to other people with the potential to abuse public funds, like the BBC, and, momentarily charities paying their CEOs huge salaries. People were beginning to distrust large enterprises and seemed to be yearning to return to a Small is Beautiful approach. The story of Dr.Shiva always hit a sympathetic spot. Our funders were happy if we could use our money to support teams like the TN. However, until Dr.Shiva managed to negotiate his way through the sluggish bureaucratic processes in Orissa, I had to continue to deliver money to him in the only way possible: wads of rupees packed between my T-shirts and delivered into his grateful hands just in time to keep the team solvent.

Chapter Thirty

A League of our own

Mastichak, Bihar

There was a collective whoop of delight from Team A as coach Madhu Singh allocated them the goal nearest the mosque. Apparently all the girls preferred this goal. A buffalo sat in a puddle of water behind the goal-posts, huge head framed by enormous curly horns and a snooty expression on its face. Perhaps it was thinking what I was thinking: better to be shooting the other way without the low, early morning sun shining into your eyes.

Madhu blew the whistle and the game started. The pace was fast, the tackles fearless, the sound effects awesome. Gone were the bare feet of a year ago, replaced by sturdy football boots. Most of the girls were still very skinny and no doubt still anaemic, but the nutritious meals they had been receiving at the hospital were making some difference, judging by their stamina and the power behind the passes. The ball was thudded across the full-sized pitch and no team dominated.

Mothers in saris crouched on the sidelines, boys leaning on cycles or slouched against the goal-posts analysed the strategies of both teams. Madhu stopped play and issued firm orders when the game got too scrappy. Sunday was the only day they were allowed to play an 11aside match but that did not mean they could forget all that they had learned during the week-day training sessions.

Suddenly the ball was at my feet. And I was in the box. It was only the third time I had touched it in the entire game. Perhaps I could redeem myself and score.

"Deedee, pass!" shouted twenty voices on the pitch.

There was only one girl I was certain was actually on my own team: Sushma with her yellow headband and pony-tail and a Rooney-10 on her yellow shirt. I passed. She scored. My team went wild with delirious delight and Deedee (elder sister) was leaped on by her wiry team-mates. I even thought I saw a satisfied smirk on the water buffalo's face.

After the game a local teacher came up to me and asked, in perfect English, if I would spend a few minutes conversing with his college students. Just tell them about your "native place" he said. Six smiling youths and I conversed for a little while, in a mixture of bad Hindi and bad English. They were not that interested in the football, but the pitch had become a central meeting place for lots of people from the surrounding villages. Here you could discuss new ideas and innovative schemes, break down old thinking and feel involved in a changing community.

The Akhand Jyoti Football Academy, linked by an umbilical cord to the eye hospital, has become a standard part of life in this corner of rural Bihar. It is probably doing more to achieve some of the United Nations Millennium Development Goals than any other scheme in the state, tackling health, education, jobs and gender inequality. But such are the preconceptions about rural Bihar that most journalists who have written about the Academy have treated the story in a light-hearted manner. Mastichak, the village name itself, lends itself to this kind of coverage. The Hindi word 'masti' coupled with 'chak', translates as "a junction for having fun". That's what these girls are doing, write the journalists, rivalling the boys in sport and having fun. The BBC World Service even made a rather predictable reference to the British film Bend it Like Beckham implying that the Bihar girls had been inspired by this film!

Of course we are all having fun playing football. But the aims and motives behind the scheme could not have been more serious and important. One girl's story brought this home to everybody.

Seema, one of the original Gang of Six with whom I had played my first game of football in Mastichak, the one in the salwar kameez and bare feet whose picture appeared in the London Times and of whom Simon Barnes wrote...well, Seema lost out. In the few weeks between my first game with them and Mritunjay establishing the Football Academy, Seema's father, who ran the local liquor store, had been offered a deal. A 45year-old village man paid him to take 15year-old Seema as his wife. He agreed with alacrity; no more school fees and one less mouth to feed. Luckily Seema's younger sister is now part of the football scheme.

I still feel sad when I think of her sister, though. That girl had so much spunk. I would have liked to have seen her in full football gear, rising through the ranks of the Mastichak girls' teams. Perhaps, like 14year-old Pooja and Soonam, she would have got into the Bihar under 16s State Team. I would have liked to have seen her training as an ophthalmic assistant, too. It would have been nice to be giving a talk on common ophthalmic disorders and see Seema sitting in the classroom. She could have graduated from the course and taken a job at the Akhand Jyoti Eye Hospital. We could have discussed differential diagnoses together. Perhaps she might even have wanted to go on to train as a doctor and have become the first ophthalmologist from the village of Mastichak.

"Deedee, ball!"

It was a high ball and I jumped to control it with my chest, and then ran with it towards the far corner of pitch where a small figure was standing. She was dressed in a yellow frock and her hair was pulled back in a high ponytail. She had been watching the bigger girls with deep concentration. She looked about five years old.

Stopping a few metres away from her I caught her eye.

"Tumko" I said, pointing directly at her, and kicked the ball, quite hard.

One little bare foot encircled with a small silver anklet, turned sideways with the poise of a Bharatanatyam dancer. She ably blocked the ball dead in its path. Then visualising the direction in which she was to send it, she kicked it back my way with a resounding thud. A pure natural. The future looked good.

CODA

The Runaway Goat

Rajasthan

The children --Azaz, Dipika, Kumlesh, Ladulal, Mukesh, Neehar, Poooja, Poonaram Rita, Suki, Suresh and Vikram, aged from five to seventeen --could not take their eyes off the two adults. 22 year-old British poet Caroline Bird sat on the floor in front of them and waved her arms around, laughing frequently and talking in a voice that echoed around the room and, hospital manager Mukesh translated into Hindi, his facial expression sometimes mirroring those of Caroline.

Through this process, Caroline had already managed to get them to think about moments in their lives when they were most happy and to throw out images of these: listening to my mother singing when I was a baby, reading the Koran, playing cricket, riding on the back of a water buffalo. She showed how these ideas could be turned around in poetry: I *am* a cricket ball flying through the air, I *am* the Koran...which made them laugh, and also got them into the swing of things.

Outside in the hospital lobby, Rajmal Jain, seated at his desk, was reading from a gift from Caroline: a collection of her published poems entitled "Trouble Came To The Turnip". He traced the English words with his finger and read them out slowly and loudly.

"When trouble came to the village
I put my love in the cabbage-cart
and we rode wrapped in cabbage
to the capital."

He roared with laughter.
"I am liking this young poet," he announced to the bemused patients and staff.

Back in the poetry workshop Caroline was trying to get the children to voice their feelings about sadness. And this was proving difficult. Even though each one of these children had been blind before cataract surgery had restored their sight, none of them mentioned any sorrow over not being able to see. They sat in thoughtful silence for a long while. Then Ladulal admitted that his saddest moment had been when he had returned home without one of his goats. As most of the children had the job of herding the village goats, they knew exactly what he meant.

"And what about the goat?" Caroline asked.

What did they think the goat was feeling?

The goat might be lost and injured, they murmured, or just lost. So the goat was probably sad, too.

Or maybe the goat was happy to have run away? explored Caroline. Perhaps it wanted to be free from the herd, to roam wherever it liked. Perhaps it thought that life outside the herd was more fun.

They were smiles and understanding head-wobbles.

I had met Caroline Bird at a poetry reading at the Wellcome Trust in London that was supposed to be about the Eye and Sight.

A very earnest young woman in black introduced the three poets. I cannot remember the names of the others but do remember that they were both male and they had both apologised for the fact that they had not written anything about the eye or sight but went on to read their poems anyway. Only Caroline seemed to have taken the brief seriously. She had written a poem especially for the occasion entitled the Monogamous Optometrist, a very funny piece about someone who undergoes surgical excision of their peripheral vision as a cure for a wandering eye! Caroline went on to describe her work with school-children: how she would encourage their imaginings by saying things like 'imagine if your eye were transplanted to your knee, what would it see? Ten years of grass it had knelt on?'

This was great stuff. And it gave me a great idea.

For World Sight Day we would celebrate by hearing poems written by children who had been cured of blindness. Caroline would go to Rajmal Jain's Shree Bhairav Eye Hospital and work with them to produce this work. The world would hear directly *from* them, not about them. Caroline was the perfect person for the job.

All the children's' poems were spectacular. But there is poignancy about their one collective poem, framed by Caroline from their own words and images. It contains a warning that all of us hoping to make the world a better place might do well to heed.

The Runaway Goat

"It's my job to bring back the goats
from the field at the end of the day
and I'm injured inside if a goat runs away.

If a goat runs away, I'm cracked
on the ground like a tea-cup of clay –
it's my job - after all - at the end of the day.

If I could pay, I'd chase my goat
over the hills in a big white bus,
a megaphone booming 'come back with us!'

'Come back with us,' the hospital says,
in their big white bus. They can't find
my goat. But they can cure the blind.

Curing the blind is a doctor's job.
Darkness. Then a festival of light.
My job is keeping the goats in sight.

Sight in both eyes can still lose a goat.
Tomorrow I will look anew.
I bet the same thing has happened to you."